HOW TO ENJOY YOUR WEEDS

BY AUDREY WYNNE HATFIELD

STERLING PUBLISHING CO., INC.   NEW YORK

OTHER BOOKS BY THE AUTHOR

Flowers to Know and Grow
  (Castle Press)
Pleasures of Herbs
  (Museum Press and St. Martin's Press)
Pleasures of Wild Plants
  (Museum Press and Taplinger
Magic of Herbs
  (Mini Corgi)

All illustrations in this book are the work of
Audrey Wynne Hatfield

Adapted for American audiences by Maryanne M. Furia and Edward W. Egan

American Edition Copyright © 1971 by
Sterling Publishing Co., Inc.
419 Park Avenue South, New York, N.Y. 10016
Original edition Copyright © 1969 by Audrey Wynne Hatfield
Manufactured in the United States of America
All rights reserved
Library of Congress Catalog Card No.: 74-167663
ISBN 0-8069-3042 –X
3043 –8

Contents

OUR HERITAGE OF WEEDS 7
Indefatigable Travelers . . . Weeds, Man's First
Staple . . . Weeds Puzzle Scientists

WEEDS LEND A HELPING HAND 13
Composting . . . Qualifications to Ponder . . .
Mother Nature's Most Potent Insecticide . . . The
Early Indians Knew . . . The Little Marigold Goes
Globe-Trotting . . . "Good Neighbors" . . . A
Gardener's Unsalaried Assistants . . . And Then
There Are the Varmints . . . Lawn Fashions
Change . . . A Search for the Prime Combination

WEEDS AS FERTILIZERS AND REMEDIES. . 32
Making Teas . . . Diet Supplements . . . Making
Wines

A WEED HERBAL 39

CHICKWEED 40

CHICORY 44

THE CLOVERS 48

COUCH GRASS 54

DANDELION 59
Dandelion Beer . . . Dandelion Wines

DAY LILY 69

DEAD NETTLES 75

FEVERFEW 82

GREAT MULLEIN 85

GROUND IVY 90

GROUNDSEL 95

HORSETAIL 100

LAMB'S-QUARTERS 106

OX-EYE DAISY 112

POTENTILLA 116

PURSLANE 123

SOAPWORT 127
   For Cleaning Fabrics

STINGING NETTLE 132

TANSY 141

TOADFLAX 146

WILD CARROT 150

WILD ROSES 155
   Rose-Petal Treats . . . Rose-Hip Products

WOOD SORREL 162

YARROW 166

WEED CONTROL 171

IDENTITY GUIDE AND INDEX 177

Our Heritage of Weeds

To ENJOY YOUR WEEDS you must know and exploit them. Living isolated in the midst of the country, surrounded by fields, woods, and thickets, I am very familiar with weeds. I have most of them and nearly all the wild plants of Hertfordshire, England. My soil must harbor great quantities of dormant seeds because every patch of ground, after being cleared for some desired planting, is almost immediately covered. These eager sproutings include not only newly awakened seedlings, but also ardent colonizers from beyond the garden wall and hedges. Either the original flora and the seed-carrying fauna resent my intrusion, or their offspring are agog to come into my cultivated, and therefore comparatively less competitive, acre. My simple choice has been to get to know them and deal with them according to their worth.

The plants we call "weeds" are either long-established wildings or survivors from past deliberate introductions, which are now invading gardens where the owners do not want them. But, strange as it may appear to some harassed gardeners, most of their hated weeds have good uses. Some make health-giving food or drink and were encouraged by our forefathers to whom they were of prime importance in those days of severely restricted diet and limited medicines. It should be remembered that they still provide the basic, well-tried remedies of the herbalist and the homeopath. (Homeopaths are those prescribers who attempt relief by means of remedies that would produce, in a healthy person, effects similar to the patient's ailment. Thus homeopathy is sometimes called "The art of curing, founded on resemblances," and these remedies are of course always administered to the sufferer in small doses. Hippocrates was the first homeopath, and it was homeopathic theory that formed the basis of Jenner's pioneering work in smallpox immunization and Pasteur's great gift to the world in developing the anti-rabies serum.)

Like all herbage, weeds have now been found to possess peculiar qualities that, when understood, can be made to contribute greatly to the robust growth of the plants we wish to cultivate. All weeds are interesting in some respect.

I am not an advocate of weedy gardens, but I am concerned with knowledgeable and enjoyable methods of coping with them. They are every gardener's concern, as no soil of any worth could be free from weeds. Some of their seeds can endure for a long time within the ground. Here, when conditions are right for their dormant preservation and when an atmosphere rightly charged with carbon dioxide surrounds them, they can sleep until the earth is disturbed. At that time they are brought to the surface, there to be awakened by light and fresh air. A famous instance of such a revival was the spectacular display of scarlet poppies arising from the newly dug graves in Flanders during the 1914–18 War.

Indefatigable Travelers

New weeds and fresh supplies of old ones continually arrive by varied means. To country or town gardens they come on currents of air. Sometimes they arrive on, or inside, migratory or native birds or animals. Even waste ground in a blackened industrial area is mysteriously sown with a collection of struggling herbage. Seeds come from near and far in packing, in mud on transport vehicles, and in cargoes. Districts around ports are sometimes enlivened with foreign plants. Most of these exotic visitors die after a season's flowering, but a few may survive as they have done in past centuries. A surprising number of seeds are carried on clothing. To prove this possibility, after a walk in the country scrape a shoe or trouser leg over a clean sheet of paper. Then empty the dust on to a tray that is spread with a layer of damp sterile peat, sterilized soil or sand, and see what germinates! Plant seeds have been carried in this way for many thousands of years, even by the earliest primitive men.

Weeds, Man's First Staple

New plants from distant countries would spring up along the tracks of early nomadic tribes. More seeds would come inside bags of grain and on the cattle accompanying the immigrant farmers of the New Stone Age, Bronze Age, and early Iron Age. Later settlers and invaders brought more seeds and left new wakes of previously unknown plants along their migratory routes. Many of these plants were even then known to be good food. There was a sensational example of this in 1950 when botanists working with archeologists were able to give a detailed description of the Tollund Man's last meal. Some corpses were recovered from early Iron Age burial grounds in the Danish raised bogs at Tollund, where they had lain for some two thousand years. One body was that of a chieftain who, considering that he had been hanged, appeared benign and serene. He was so perfectly preserved in the peat, save for a bent nose, that botanists were able to analyze his stomach contents and found the remains of his last meal. This had consisted of a gruel made from roughly ground seeds. A large proportion of linseed and barley was mixed with smaller amounts of "weeds"—such wild plants as pale persicaria, black bindweed, gold of pleasure, lamb's-quarters, hemp nettle, wild pansy, and corn spurry.

This gruel would be more nutritious than today's breakfast cereals, as it was rich in proteins and vitamins. The pansy seeds would give it a mildly stimulating effect for the heart and respiratory organs. They were also a gentle laxative. Ample evidence was discovered to prove that all these plants were deliberately collected or cultivated by those people. As most of them were wild plants native also to Britain, they would be encouraged there and consumed in the same way. Corn spurry was actually introduced into Britain with linseed (flax) at that time in the early Iron Age and in Roman times, and for centuries later, it was grown as a crop for its oily seeds.

During the three hundred years of the busy comings and goings of the Roman occupation of Britain the native flora were enriched by quantities of exotic seeds that were brought in from all over Europe and Asia. Some were deliberate introductions, to be cultivated as customary Latin food and medicines or to provide the cosmetics and the floral decorations that were necessary adornments of sophisticated Roman living. Other seeds were accidentally spread about from the packings of imports and from the clothing and equipment of the much-traveled Roman legions who built and used the new roads, nearly seven thousand miles of them from end to end of Britain. An early observer, Dr. John Dee, who lived in the times of Queen Elizabeth I, recorded how he found medicinal herbs of the types planted by the Romans still growing alongside the ruins of the fortified wall built during the reign of their Emperor Hadrian. When we know our plants, we find not only Roman introductions, but numerous older and also some more recent romantic ones, still flourishing in British gardens. Any weed is more enjoyable when we know something interesting about its associations and its ancient uses.

Weeds Puzzle Scientists

Nowadays we have abundant evidence of the periods when certain plants existed in different areas of Great Britain. Their fossil remains, pollen, and seeds are to be found in various strata of the land. Many geological excavations have yielded important discoveries. The most puzzling of these, however, occur when examination of a soil stratum reveals the isolated remains of some particular plant and yet, until then, our earliest evidence of this plant's existence in Britain belonged to a period far later than the soil of this particular geological era. Such was the case with *Lactuca sativa,* a type of lettuce native to Southwest Asia or Siberia. Who brought this plant to Britain so that it grew on the levels of the Mesolithic settlement on the Isle of Wight? (Here six perfect seeds were found.) It was only later, millenniums later, that the *Lactuca sativa* was introduced into Europe and became our salad plant! Unlike our native wild lettuces, this species would have been too tender to survive unaided and multiply into one of the weeds we find difficult to control.

Our garden weeds, from small annuals to greedy perennials, are, in general, plants that have persisted through all their struggles with the earth's great changes and catastrophes. These hardy survivors have been mercilessly shifted about by earthquakes, glaciers, floods, and avalanches. They have endured periods of intense cold and intense heat, all the while becoming less sensitive to types of soil and climate and evolving those aggressive methods of defense which defeat our efforts but must evoke our interest and respect. A few of these survivors became self-fertilizing so that they need not rely on either insects or wind. Some developed roots that could run underground like trains, thrusting through such solid obstacles as our potatoes and sending up shoots that surface at short or long intervals to become independent, menacing plants. Others traveled above ground, rooting as they progressed and forming their complicated networks of abundant colonies.

Certain of our weeds developed a cunning capacity for staggering their germination timing instead of simultaneously ripening. A number of their fruits could germinate almost as soon as they touched the ground. Others were delayed for an interval of time, and the rest remained dormant for months. This ensured that some offspring would survive even if others encountered impossible weather, the gardener's hoe, or other uncongenial conditions.

Weeds of all kinds appear to have evolved marvelous tricks to tease and embarrass gardeners. They are by nature the determined plants that have been the most tolerant and are now the most successful. We could never for long be free of them and we would be the poorer without them.

Weeds Lend
a Helping Hand

A GOOD GARDEN SOIL should contain quantities of the nutrient or "fertilizing" elements, nitrogen, phosphorus, and potassium. Smaller amounts of magnesium and sulphur should be present, but these also should predominate over the minor or "trace" elements such as iron, zinc, manganese, copper, cobalt, boron, and the rare base metal molybdenum. The other soil constituents will, of course, be determined by the rock foundation and the mineral content of the site. These are naturally sought and assimilated by plants as they are necessary for their well-being. They are also essential for our well-being, and we can get them only directly or indirectly through our edible crops or the varied pastures where cattle graze. If these elements are absent from our garden soil or if they are rendered unavailable through too high a lime content, we and our plants suffer from their deficiency. Some plants choose and take up a greater amount of one element than do others. For instance, we value spinach for its iron and vitamin content, but some weeds are much richer in these and other essentials. So it follows that when we "weed" our gardens we take out plants that have robbed the soil. But these plants have not only stored some of the soil's vital components. They have manufactured certain valuable secretions. If we take away a weed, which may be either a miser of some valuable element or the waste from a harvested vegetable, and if we burn it in a bonfire, then we seriously deplete our soil and rob desirable plants not only of their elemental requirements but also of humus. (Humus is the organic portion of any soil. It consists of either animal or vegetable matter in a state of partial decay.)

A gardener's responsibility is to return everything he takes from his ground. Bonfires should be kindled merely to burn such things as woody prunings, old stakes, and pea and bean sticks. The conscientious gardener will add to his bonfire lumps of hard clay of a type that becomes red and reduces itself to powder when burnt, because such clay is rich in mineral salts and, when blended with the wood ash, will make an excellent addition to the soil. Note, however, that this mixture should *never* be used near mint because mint is badly affected by any bonfire ash.

Composting

Everything that is taken from the soil goes back to it, and with interest, by composting. Every weed, haulm (the stems of cultivated plants such as beans and cereals after the crops have been gathered in), and leaf, all lawn mowings, with kitchen waste, torn-up paper (not grease-proof), vacuum-cleaner dust and fluff, feathers, hay, straw, and any available waste from a fish market or grocery store should go into the compost heap. This collection becomes one of the pleasures of gardening, rather like preparing tasty banquets, with weeds providing the "seasoning" and valuable nutrients.

An efficient heap should measure about 6 feet by 4 feet

and it must sufficiently heat up to consume weed seeds and their most persistent roots that are a prime source of indispensable plant food. The sides of the heap should be enclosed to prevent currents of air from keeping the margins cool. This can be achieved in several ways. One is to stack squares of turf grass-side down so that side walls are formed around the site. Another way is to make wooden sides around the compost pile by means of planks fixed to upright supports. In this type of solution the gardener must arrange his construction so that one end is movable, for easy removal of the composted stuff. An efficient cagelike structure can be made with wire netting fastened to stakes driven into the ground. Here the gardener must leave one end hinged to open, or separate, so that it may be lifted away. To retain the heat that is generated, this light open pen must be lined with straw, or with sheets of newspaper that are turned into the compost as they rot and are replaced with sound ones. However it is constructed, the heap must stand on bare earth, which allows the necessary soil bacteria to enter the waste matter and do its job of breaking down and decomposing.

The materials to be composted should be placed in layers about 6 inches thick. They should be sandwiched with thinner layers of soil and garnished with a few sprays of aromatic herbs and a sprinkling of a properly balanced and blended herbal activator. Or the activator may be made from seaweed, which is rich in all the basic elements that are washed into the sea from river beds. Either of these is far superior to chemicals that are sold for the purpose.

When the heap reaches 3 or 4 feet in height the contents

must be covered and sealed with soil like a potato clamp. All the materials will soon rot down to a rich humus containing most of the soil's requirements, and it should look as appetizing as dark, crumbly Christmas pudding.

QUALIFICATIONS TO PONDER

No plants are fit for the compost heap if they have been poisoned or sprayed with a chemical pesticide (insect killer). And grass is not eligible if it has been mown from a lawn that has been given any selective (hormone) weed killer. But if lawn sand has been used, the mowings are good.

If the compost heap can be made under an elderberry bush or a birch tree, the excretions from their roots, together with their fallen leaves, will assist fermentation, making the compost light and especially effective for restoring the soil.

Well-rotted compost is of greatest value as a top or near-top dressing that will be gradually washed down to the plant roots. It is too precious to bury deeply as it will go down too far for them to reach. When digging a bed for planting, any weeds, excluding the live roots of perennials, should be put in nearly a foot deep and chopped with a sharp spade. Next cover them with uncomposted kitchen waste and, finally, top with soil and compost. I have had spectacular results with this method. The plant roots seem to hurry down to the eggshells, tea leaves, peel, fish, vegetable waste, and weeds, producing strong, healthy top growth as they gorge.

Mother Nature's Most Potent Insecticide

The value of weeds in the compost heap and back into the soil where they came from is probably even greater than we yet realize, as new evidence of the power of plants is being continually observed. An exciting discovery of recent years was made by a Dutch nurseryman who planted African marigolds of the variety Colorado Sunshine (*Tagetes erecta*) as a cut-flower crop after removing his daffodil bulbs. Finding that the marigolds had destroyed his nematode soil pest, the narcissus eelworm, he passed the information to a research station. There experiments were started with various kinds of Tagetes. The nurseryman had happened on a lucky choice, as the hybrids he might have chosen for cut blooms gave no such pesticide results. It was found however, that both the so-called African and the French marigold (*Tagetes patula*), which are really Mexican wild plants, could kill other plant-destroying nematodes too, and at a range of 3 feet. Fortunately, the beneficial types of eelworms which do not feed on healthy roots were not affected.

The details of more experiments with various Tagetes species make too long a story for this book, but an English research association pursuing their tests with a *Tagetes minuta*, direct from its native Mexico, found this plant dealt with all kinds of destructive eelworms and also dismissed wireworms, millepedes, and various root-eating pests from its vicinity. Astoundingly, it in many instances even killed couch grass, convolvulus, ground ivy, ground elder, horsetail, and other persistent weeds that defy most poisons. Its lethal action worked only on starchy roots and had no effect on woody ones like roses, fruit bushes, and shrubs. Where it had grown, the soil was enriched as well as cleansed, its texture was refined, and lumps of clay were broken up.

THE EARLY INDIANS KNEW

According to archeological findings, this Mexican weed's powers were no new discovery. On vases buried with the Chimu farmers and gardeners of ancient Ecuador and on the grave furniture of the Chavins of pre-Inca Peru, we find flower umbels of the *Tagetes minuta* painted right alongside pictures of these peoples' food crops. Significantly, the Chimu and the Chavins belong to two civilizations that thousands of years ago grew potatoes, tomatoes, runner and French beans, maize, and other crops we also value. This was the plant sacred to their gods of agriculture, and for good reason. For it was the *Tagetes minuta* that enabled those peoples, who had very restricted areas of usable land, to grow continually and successfully on the same ground, plants that shared the same eelworm risks. We could not grow such crops on the same ground for more than two years without inviting trouble. Yet some of those areas were cultivated without rest or rotation for two thousand years, with unsophisticated sea-bird guano, fish waste, and Tagetes. Without this protective herb the cultivated plants would certainly have soon become the victims of eelworms and perished. To those ancient farmers without equipment to see the pests, their crop failures would appear to be the curse of their gods.

THE LITTLE MARIGOLD GOES GLOBE-TROTTING

The story of this Mexican marigold exemplifies various aspects of most plants. Its rapid and wide distribution as a weed has been recent enough to be traced. It is a lusty

TAGETES MINUTA

annual of giant size, with umbels of small, cream, disclike flowers, and the seeds were sent from Mexico to an Australian park, to be grown there as a rare plant with decorative foliage. It was so happy in that park that its seeds ripened, and by all the methods of transport which seeds can use, they traveled over Australia to become a common weed. During the 1914–18 War some seeds accidentally arrived in South Africa in the fodder for the horses of the Australian artillery. This marigold liked that country, too, and romped away as a flourishing weed. In Rhodesia, the powerful secretions and excretions of this now common weed provide a cheap and effective answer to some tobacco growers' problems. It attacks their soil pests and other weeds, and the liquid from the marigold leaves after they have been boiled makes a very efficient pesticide spray. In this respect, the Tagetes is an outstanding example of all plants' ability to manufacture their own brand of secretion which is characteristic of their family, although the members of each plant family (the species) vary considerably in their accumulations. Plants of the genus Tagetes are members of the *Compositae* family, the daisy tribe. And while all daisy-flowered plants produce much the same substances in greatly varying degrees, *Tagetes minuta* by far outdoes them all in quantity and potency. But the same natural pesticide compound is made by its relation, the wild pyrethrum of Africa, and this has been available for many years as about the safest of all pesticides that are commercially exploited.

"Good Neighbors"

It is obvious that the compounds that plants excrete through their roots have a direct influence on the vitality of the soil. Some stimulate the growth of valuable organisms. Others poison the necessary bacteria. Less obvious is the effect of their exhalations, that is, the scents of their volatile substances. It is these usually subtle odors that make them acceptable or repellent to other types. A noticeable example, however, is the ethylene gas breathed out by some ripening fruits, especially apples, bananas, tomatoes, peaches, and avocados. When they are in a room near such fruits, daffodils and carnations can be seen to suffer from the gas, and roses are sickened by it to a lesser degree. Ethylene is also generated by damaged leaves of green vegetables in the garden.

Another instance of the reality of these substances is the particular breath of violets. Violet exhalations numb the nerves that control the sense of smell in human beings. As a result, gardeners who grow a lot of these flowers are unable to enjoy their fragrance.

With all these influences it is obvious that plants must be great individualists, and anyone who has tended a garden for many seasons will have become aware that they have their affinities and their enemies among other plants. Some will thrive in one place, but will not even try in another. Often this is because their bedfellows are either sympathetic and encouraging or detrimental and stunting. Few of us can boast of an herbaceous border where some plants have not appeared sadly defeated even though their soil requirements have been supplied, and many a gardener has been puzzled by some failure in his vegetable plot. These disappointments can be caused by the lack of suitable influences or the presence of plant aversions. To avoid them we should aim at the knowledgeable placing together of sympathetic plants.

I have experienced unmistakable instances of this plant symbiosis and I have heard of and read about others that I can easily accept. Although these relationships apply equally to weeds, they are easier to appreciate with cultivated plants. For instance, the *Alliums,* members of the onion tribe, are so rich in their sulphur secretions, excretions, and "breath" that they can greatly influence other plants. Garlic, chives, and shallots appear to be good neighbors to most garden plants except peas and beans, who hate them and are noticeably retarded when oniony plants are nearby. My broad beans are usually excellent, but they failed twice when grown near shallots. Peas and beans prefer carrots and turnips as neighbors. Broad beans are happy, too, near early potatoes and, curiously, they will tolerate leeks. Carrots are so encouraged by the friendly chives and shallots that they grow larger, stronger, and more flavorous when near them. Carrots and leeks do well together, and the leeks discourage the carrot-fly pest.

Roses are vastly improved in stamina, and their scent is doubled by the proximity of anything oniony. They relish garlic so much that in some countries where they are commercially cultivated for perfumes, garlic is grown with them. In a private garden this particular companionship may be, aesthetically, difficult to provide, but it pays to use all the onion waste as a mulch for our roses. Also we can plant among them ornamental members of the Allium family, such as the golden garlic (*Allium moly*), which has wide straplike leaves and round clusters of large, brilliant yellow blooms, and the giant chives (*A. schoenoprasum sibiricum*) with their narrow leaves and rose-purple flower heads. There are more of these decorative

DECORATIVE ALLIUM

23

onions that we and our roses will enjoy, and in a kitchen emergency their leaves can supply an onion flavor.

Moreover, I have found that roses grown near any member of the onion family suffer less from black spot than do roses that are planted away from this affinity. As this disease is serious only in pure air and does not occur near industrial districts, I wonder if the sulphurous volatile oil that is characteristic of the *Alliums* has a deterrent effect similar to the sulphur in smoke fumes.

Roses have another friend in parsley, and they aid each other in several ways. For many years they have been planted together to their mutual benefit in at least one famous garden, where it has been found that the parsley greatly reduces the roses' aphis attacks. This friendly herb also assists tomatoes and asparagus, which are excellent bedfellows, and the three companions fight one another's soil pests.

The tomato is one of the few cultivated plants with particular root excretions that can vanquish the extremely persistent weed, couch grass. I read of this curious conquest long after I had actually experienced it. During World War II, I rented half an acre of a field to grow tomatoes for the Marketing Board. It was a mass of couch grass, but I dug and manured it and hopefully put in thousands of tomato plants. They yielded some tons of fruits, and the couch grass disappeared from their beds although it remained around the plot.

Tomatoes are wonderfully sympathetic to the cabbage tribe. The helpful effect of aromatic herbs on the cabbages is quite remarkable, especially sage, rosemary, mint, thyme, and lavender. In fact, aromatic herbs are the most popular of plant associates and should be lavishly included

CAMOMILE

in any garden. They have an invigorating effect on most plants and a repellent effect on many destructive insects above and below ground. Such pests as the cabbage fly are put off by their scents. Some authorities claim that hyssop is the encouraging herb to plant under a grape vine as it increases the yield and the quality of the fruit. While camomile assists most things, the cabbages thrive in its vicinity. And because the common camomile does not mind being trodden down but breathes its scent more strongly when crushed, it makes a delightful subject for permanent paths between crops in the vegetable plot or anywhere else in the garden. This herb was once known as the plants' physician, since when it was placed near a sickly one it soon recovered. Among the aromatic herbs, rue is the opponent of sage and sweet basil, for if they are put into the same bed one or all will give up and die.

Lettuce and carrots are mates, as are lettuce and strawberries. Long ago an affinity was experienced by some old gardeners who recorded that strawberries had a curious liking for pine and spruce which was not shared by other plants. When pine needles were given to them as a mulch, with token twigs and cones placed on their beds, the strawberry plants were more vigorous and their fruits had an excellent flavor. This observation is quite true.

These plants have another sympathetic companion in borage, which gives them an extra fillip. Borage is a helpful plant anywhere in the garden and is a generous source of potassium, calcium, and mineral salts in the soil and in the compost.

A GARDENER'S UNSALARIED ASSISTANTS

Those lovely flowering plants, foxgloves, are really a

YELLOW PERENNIAL FOXGLOVES

necessary inclusion in any garden as they encourage
neighboring plants while stimulating their growth and
endurance. The storage of potatoes and other root
vegetables is most successful when they have been grown

with foxgloves nearby. Indoors, their bloom-spires help to preserve other cut flowers. Moreover, if some of the tea made from foxglove leaves is put into the water for floral arrangements, they will last much longer than when foxglove's influence is lacking. There are many beautiful species of perennial foxgloves which are an asset to any border.

Nasturtiums are another gardener's ally. The pungent essence they secrete is obnoxious to such plant pests as aphis and white fly, and the excretion from their roots into the surrounding soil not only scares root-lice but furthermore is taken up by other plants so that they too are less attractive to pests. Climbing nasturtiums are often placed around apple trees to thwart woolly aphis and they are grown in greenhouses to frustrate a variety of destructive pests.

AND THEN THERE ARE THE VARMINTS

The worst villains in any garden are the buttercup tribe, the *Ranunculaceae,* which give nothing but take all the good things available and seriously deplete the ground of potassium and other elements. The secretions from their roots poison the precious nitrogen bacteria in the soil so that other plants suffer from their deficiency. When the weed varieties, the bulbous or creeping buttercups—or crowfoots as they are often called—get into a strawberry, pea, or bean bed, they will dwarf these plants and cause them to panic into producing premature, small fruits. This greedy, selfish family is a large one and includes such various members as the delphinium, peony, anemone, and clematis, and many another desirable garden subject. Even these highly prized members of the *Ranunculaceae* family share the common buttercup's incompatibility with other plants, so that their beds and their neighbors' require constant feeding and replenishing.

Another garden favorite of dubious character and breath is the gladiolus. It has been noticed that a bed containing a collection of these showy plants inhibited peas and beans as far away as 50 feet!

It must be obvious that weeds react in the same ways as cultivated plants, secreting, excreting, and exhaling their characteristic substances that make them good or bad neighbors, and this important aspect of weeds will be included in their separate descriptions.

Lawn Fashions Change

A private lawn is the one place in a garden where masses of thriving companionable "weeds" can be enjoyed and where their careful assembling succeeds aesthetically and practically. Weed-free turf is now considered necessary for special games, although it is believed Sir Francis Drake rolled his famous bowls on a camomile green. (In 1588 the British naval hero was thoroughly enjoying himself in this popular lawn sport when the frantic news was brought to him that the Spanish fleet had begun its invasion of Britain. But so engrossed was Drake that he refused to meet the onslaught of the Spanish Armada until he had finished his game. And this aplomb secured for both the game and his camomile lawn, a permanent place in Western history.)

However, weedless turf is a bothersome and highly expensive ambition to strive for, and maintain, in a private garden or lawnsite today. I am not suggesting that we go back to medieval lawns which were artistic imitations of natural meadows "starred with a thousand flowers," as we see them in beautiful old tapestries and paintings. These were succeeded by the delightful camomile lawns, the first of the specialized sowings, which were popular with the purists for several centuries when labor was plentiful and cheap. In those days, grasses were the hated weeds, but the garden boys would creep along the lawn picking them out. Now that grass has become our ideal lawn plant, and as other weeds inevitably intrude and garden boys have vanished, our most sensible course is surely to encourage and actually introduce the right weeds. These happen to grow in lawns almost anywhere and they are among the most difficult to control. By using them, we work in Nature's way and with natural help that is free. Yet the result will be a more than ordinarily beautiful, serviceable, and scented lawn, which will remain green when others are yellowing.

A SEARCH FOR THE PRIME COMBINATION

The right weeds are the grass's affinities and its staunchest allies are the clovers. For the tightest growth, white or Dutch clover (*Trifolium repens*) and suckling clover or lesser yellow trefoil (*T. dubium*) are the best kinds to introduce along with other friendly herbs. These are the bottle-green, feathery-leaved yarrow (*Achillea millefolium*) and the dusky-leaved creeping thyme (*Thymus serpyllum*), whose pungent scent was used on the chests of the elegant Greek and Roman males as the perfume of all manly virtues. There should also be the grayish-green foliage of the common camomile (*Anthemis nobilis*), which smells of apples when crushed. This must not be allowed to flower as it will then become straggly. The colors, textures, and delicious scents of the thyme and camomile are memorable features of the turf on the Cornish cliffs, as well as in parts of Surrey and other places in rural England where they grow wild.

With this sympathetic mixture we gain a richly colored lawn that is permanently and perfectly fertilized. The clovers, besides being a source of sodium, encourage and store the nitrogen-fixing bacteria in their root nodules. Thus, even in the hottest and driest summers a plentiful supply of these elements is available to keep the grass lush and brilliantly green. The yarrow provides copper, nitrates, phosphates, and potash. The camomile gives calcium, and the thyme has other gifts. All that is required from the gardener is an annual dressing of the composted mowings, with dried blood and bonemeal to keep the clover in good heart so that it can nourish the grass.

The texture of this turf is thickened to that of a deep, resilient pile, since with the regular mowing, the clover and other plants produce smaller and smaller leaves as they become prostrate and more dense. Unwanted weeds are likely to be smothered. However, if buttercups should sneak in and be allowed to develop, they will kill the clovers.

It is interesting that this "weed" mixture, which has produced many fine lawns, was evolved after the 1914–18 War for the Imperial War Graves Commission. They used it all over Europe to make the wonderful, fragrant turf of their huge cemeteries, where it has withstood the varying climatic and soil conditions and the treading of many thousands of visitors.

Weeds as Fertilizers and Remedies

WHEN WE KNOW that certain weeds are especially retentive of various elements that would benefit our cultivated plants, it is enjoyable and profitable to make the weeds into the most natural of liquid fertilizers. These are then watered on the roots of more deserving subjects. The liquids may also be sprayed on plants to be quickly absorbed by the leaves as folia feeds, and some of them act as insect repellents at the same time. For this purpose, the young weeds should be gathered in the early morning before they are affected by sunshine. They may be used fresh from the garden or they may be dried in a shady place to be stored in tins for future use.

To make the liquids, cover a handful of the fresh weeds or a tablespoonful of the dried, powdered ones with 20 ounces of water and bring it just to a boil. Then remove the pan from the heat, keeping it covered as it cools. Strain the liquid free from any bits that would clog the spray and dilute it with four parts of water. Stir for 10 minutes, adding a dessertspoonful of liquid soap, the washing-up kind. This helps the stuff to adhere to the foliage when it is being sprayed as a folia feed. The liquid should be used as soon as possible after it is cool and blended. When the infusion is intended to be used only as a root fertilizer, do not add the liquid soap.

As our need of elements and plant constituents is very important too, it is equally satisfying to know that some of our weeds can give them to us as well as to our plants. One man's weed can be another man's comforting herb when he appreciates its possibilities. The teas that are infused from some weeds are really beneficial for us all. If any gardeners are doubtful of their weeds' values I suggest they consult a list of medicinal plants from an herb or health food shop. They may be surprised to recognize the items and their cost. For instance, a packet of dried couch-grass roots is priced around 50 cents, and such recommended weeds as dandelion and nettles are equally expensive. Even the most doubting gardener must know that the study of plants' curative qualities is nearly as old as history, that it was the beginning of medicine, and that it is still greatly involved with that science. And just as foxgloves provide digitalis for relieving heart disorders, so other plants can claim curative virtues that have been established over the centuries. The particular efficacies of our most useful weeds are given in their individual descriptions, but as most of the teas are made in the same way, to save repetition I will give the method here.

Making Teas

Pour 10 ounces of boiling water over a handful of fresh leaves or a level teaspoonful of dried ones . . . that is, a ratio of 1 ounce of leaves to $1\frac{1}{4}$ pints of boiling water. From this simple formula we have now obtained an infusion, water in which a substance has been steeped until its particular virtues have been extracted and permeate the liquid. Be sure to keep the infusions covered while they cool, to prevent the *virtuous steam* from escaping. The tisanes (tisanes are infusions that have medicinal value because they have been formed from herbs, flowers, or herbal parts) may be sweetened with honey and flavored with a squeeze of lemon juice. I must emphasize the benefit of drinking at least half a pint of these teas daily. They should be varied during the week and should *always* be made from three or four kinds of plants because the leaves appear to work better when in company than when alone with their own kind. I believe dandelion to be the most beneficial of all herbs. Therefore I always put three or five leaves, according to their size, into any tisane to be sure of absorbing their precious vitamin content and the iron and copper they accumulate. Recent investigations have shown that iron cannot be assimilated by humans unless a trace of copper is present in the food, and this makes the dandelion exceedingly valuable as a guard against anemia and other deficiencies.

For general well-being, the plants should be chosen for their aid in maintaining the all-around healthy functioning of the body—with a lean toward remedying one's own organic weaknesses.

Any medicinal teas that are made for the gardener's own comfort can be used, too, as liquid fertilizer for his plants' benefit.

Diet Supplements

A few weeds that are especially rich in the health-giving elements and vitamins can be eaten as tasty vegetables. These will be especially enjoyed when the garden supply of crops is meager. In some cases, the weed's value in our diet is greater than that of the usual vegetables we eat. This is certainly true where vegetables have been reared commercially and have absorbed the poisonous pesticides that are now in common use. Some years ago this danger struck American canners of baby foods, as the vegetables supplied to them were found to contain lethal components of the pesticides used in their cultivation. These manufacturers had to insist that the crops be grown in compost and without such chemical aids.

Now, having urged the gardener to take his weeds as medicine and to eat them as vegetables and salads, I will suggest that he drink them for pleasure. There are some refreshing and invigorating beers to be brewed from weeds and there are the wines, which can be very good. These are surely appropriate ways to enjoy our weeds most.

The process of making these country wines is dealt with at length in a number of excellent books devoted to the subject. They explain the methods of producing them dry, sweet, still, or sparkling, but their instructions are far too long for my space. I shall therefore give only the simple process stage by stage, hoping it will be easy to follow and that it will produce enjoyable and festive results. The first stage of each brew is given with its recipe in the individual plant's description. However, since from the second stage to the final bottling, the process is the same for all the wines, the method is given here to save more needless repetition.

Making Wines

The ingredients according to the recipe are put into a large vessel (an earthenware crock is good, or a plastic bucket). This should be capable of holding more than the quantity to be fermented to allow for the frothing. A wooden spoon must be used for stirring, as no metal other than aluminum or stainless steel should ever touch the wine to taint its flavor.

When all the ingredients are in the vessel it must be covered with three or four layers of clean cotton cloth tied down. This serves to keep out the tiny vinegar-making flies that will be attracted to the contents. It is left in a warm room for a week or two and should be stirred and squeezed daily, until the exuberant bubbling is over.

Although most wine recipes tell us to add all the sugar (see various Wine Recipes throughout the book) at once, the brew will be much better if you start with one-third of the recommended amount. Then, when fermentation is active, add the second one-third. And two weeks after that, pour in the last of the sugar.

STAGE 2. The contents of the vessel are now ladled out and strained through a plastic, aluminum, or enameled colander into another clean vessel. A plastic bucket or a large bowl is useful to receive the strained liquid. This operation takes out the solid refuse. Then the liquid must be again strained over a large jug through a hair sieve or the colander. This time several thicknesses of cheesecloth, or one of organdie muslin, must be laid over the straining utensil to trap the bits and the sediment.

The clear liquid is now ready to be poured through a nonmetal funnel into a glass fermentation jar and lightly sealed with an air lock. The transparent glass jar is good because you can see how the wine behaves. Both the jars and the air locks can be bought quite cheaply from any store that sells wine-making utensils. A cheap air lock made of plastic is a clever device, as it holds a little water to trap the gases from the fermenting wine but excludes the air from outside. When dry, an air-lock cork is too big to fix into the neck of a jar, but if it is soaked in boiling water and lightly beaten, it eventually obeys.

When the fermentation jar is filled and sealed it should be kept in a warm room or in an airing cupboard, in as even a temperature as possible, for two or three weeks. Then it is ready to be moved to a cool place for another fortnight or longer, until the little bubbles do not rise to the surface when the jar is moved.

STAGE 3. There will now be a sediment of spent yeast on the bottom of the jar. Because this will spoil the wine's flavor if it is not removed, the wine must be siphoned or "racked" off into a clean jar. This operation requires 4 feet of $\frac{1}{2}$-inch-diameter rubber tubing, as sold in any drugstore.

To siphon off, stand the jar containing the wine on a table, and the clean jar on the floor. Insert one end of the tube into the wine above the sediment and suck the other end until the wine flows down the tube. Now put this end quickly into the clean jar and let it flow, leaving the brown sediment behind. Insert the air lock tightly closed and leave the jar in a cool place.

As more sediment forms, rack it again, and again if necessary, until the wine remains crystal-clear for a week or two. At that time it will be ready for bottling. This perfect clearing usually takes about three or four months, sometimes longer, but bottling must not be attempted so long as there is any sign of sediment forming.

STAGE 4. Champagne bottles, or any other good thick wine bottles with an indentation in the base, are the best to use. Some hotels are quite glad to get rid of their empties. Before filling, the bottles must be well washed and thoroughly rinsed, then dried in a warm oven and cooled with a plug of absorbent cotton in the tops to keep them sterilized.

To fill the bottles, stand the jar holding the wine on a table and place the bottle on the floor on a tray. Now insert the tube into the wine as for racking, suck the end until the wine flows, and then put the tube into the bottle and fill up to about 1 inch from the cork.

Use new straight-sided corks and soften them in boiling water. To drive the corks well home it is advisable to invest in a cork-hammer. This gadget is quite cheap. This is fortunate because without one it is nearly impossible to get the cork completely into the bottle neck. With a cork-hammer, however, you just give it one sock with the wooden mallet and the cork is driven perfectly home. Store the bottles on their sides in a cool dark place or wrap paper around them to keep out the light. Do not be too anxious to sample the wine as it may not even be palatable for months. Let it mature for about a year, when it should be delicious.

A Weed Herbal

HERE FOLLOWS MY little herbal of some familiar and useful "weeds." Unfortunately, we have corrupted this word and its meaning. Originally the word was *wèods*, and it was the Anglo-Saxon name for all herbs or small plants. Some plants these early people of Britain called *wyrt*, and our present-day term "wort" is derived from this Old English word.

To past generations of men, all plants were regarded with respect—some with affection and some with fear. None, however, was held in contempt. Many plants were either food or medicine, or else they possessed religious or magical influences. A number of the plants we scorn today as our inglorious "weeds" were ready and waiting with their health-giving properties to serve man and beast long before grasses had fat kernels, or root crops had thick tubers, or trees had large, juicy fruits. To them we owe our earliest ancestors' survival. And to later prehistoric men, they gave health and the strength for the human race to progress. We should never belittle the original and constant value of such herbs.

Chickweed

CHICKWEED is also known as chick wittles, chicknyweed, clucken wort, skirt buttons, and star chickweed. There are many varieties of chickweed, but the one I am concerned with is the light green, succulent, edible weed that comes up on any good, bared ground. And it must not be confused with the dark green, tough-looking, whiskery mouse-ear chickweed that infests lawns. The eatable star chickweed is smooth, and its translucent stems have only a single line of fine hairs which runs up the stems to a joint, then stops and changes sides to continue on to the next node. It has as glamorous a name as any prima donna — *Stellaria media*. This name survives from medieval times as the description of the tiny, white star-shaped flowers of its genus. Its species name, *media*, indicates that it is the middle-sized member of the clan. The chickweeds come from a family with rather splendid members: the *Caryophyllaceae*. Thus, this small, modest weed is cousin to the bold carnation.

Chickweed is an annual that lasts through winter and seldom lacks flowers and seeds. This is strange because it has but a threadlike hold in the ground, and its delicate stems and pointed oval leaves appear too fragile to survive any severe weather. It is an unusually cosmopolitan plant, for not only does it grow throughout Europe and southern and central Asia (traveling eagerly wherever and whenever white settlers have gone into temperate lands), but it is

CHICKWEED

even established in the Arctic Circle. Therefore, the fact that chickweed fossils have been found in the Lea Valley Arctic Bed and in the soil stratum of Britain's late-glacial period should not surprise us. Furthermore, the geological records of chickweed become widespread and uninterrupted for those eras when the forests of Britain were cleared and these cleared areas inhabited. Thus, we get an excellent picture of chickweed's vigor and abundance.

This friendly herb is among the few plants possessing a rich copper content. This, along with its other valuable constituents, makes it a highly beneficial cress in the diet of man, beast, and bird. For cress it is, and such a good one that it was once hawked in city streets and sold in bundles to make salads, to be cooked as a tender vegetable, or to be made into the effective poultices for which it was famed (as a cure for abscesses and carbuncles). Also, it was infused into a tea to comfort troubled stomachs or slim down fat citizens. As a lotion, the infusion was soothing to the eyes.

Chickweed is still sold in some British shops to refresh "Little birds in cadges . . . when they loath their meate"— just as the Tudor herbalist Gerard writes. With the groundsel plant it has today relapsed into a birds' treat. Herbalists, however, continue to value its soothing, cooling, and curative qualities. And, therefore, it is retained as an ingredient in many of their medicines and ointments. Unfortunately, chickweed has fallen out of use as a culinary herb, and this neglect can be explained only by the fact that most contemporary gardeners are unaware of its virtues. I like it and encourage it enough for salads. But for the quantities necessary to cook as a vegetable, I go to a nearby field.

As a cress to be put in salads, wash the plants and shake them dry in a cloth. For sandwiches chickweed can be given a fillip by a squeeze of lemon juice, a seasoning of salt and pepper, and a few drops of Worcestershire sauce on the bread and butter. Like any cress, this one goes well with tomato or any other sandwich filling.

As a delicious vegetable, chickweed is very like the tenderest early spring spinach (but some people and children like it better) and it is equally wholesome. A good quantity of these little plants is needed as they shrink when boiled. Wash them and put them into a pan without shaking off the water. Add a dab of butter and a light seasoning of salt and pepper. Now put in some chopped chives, shallots, or spring onions and a sprinkling of nutmeg. Cook carefully to avoid burning. Drain and serve hot. A squeeze of lemon juice before serving gives the vegetable a piquancy that is good with rich meats.

As a tea or tisane, gather a good handful of the plants, wash them, and pour 10 ounces of boiling water over them. The thin yellow peel of a lemon or orange may be added for flavoring. Cover the vessel to prevent the steam from escaping. Drink this amount daily in several doses to relieve constipation, to soothe an upset stomach, or to act as a helpful slimming potion of ancient reputation. The same infusion makes an excellent lotion to relieve tired or inflamed eyes.

As an effective poultice to cure carbuncles and abscesses, place the herbs in a cheesecloth or muslin bag and boil them for a minute. Then apply hot, but not scalding. Use the water to bathe the sore.

Chicory

CHICORY, succory, wild succory. *Barbe de capucin* is the French name for these blanched leaves that are so much liked for salads. The English herbalist Parkinson, a seventeenth-century royal apothecary, says succory is a "fine, cleansing, jovial plant." Only twice has this jovial plant arrived uninvited into my garden, but I have bought it and grown it to be used many times. The beautiful blue of the flowers is a great pleasure when grouped in an herb border as a foil to tall green-leaved subjects and shorter gray-leaved ones.

The plant is properly called *Cichorium intybus* and it is closely related to the annual or biennial endive, *C. endivia,* which is a native of southern Asia. Chicory's long taproot prefers a light, sandy soil so that it flourishes on wastelands, waysides, and field borders. It grows about 3 feet tall and has stiff, angular stems. Its spreading branches, given off at a considerable angle, are sparsely clothed with dandelionlike, toothed leaves. However, the stems produce a profusion of leaves and flowers, and the numerous bright blue flower heads nestle in the leaf axils in clusters of two or three. They are rather large when fully expanded at definite times of the day. Their opening and closing is so reliable that the great botanist Linneaus used chicory in his floral clock at Uppsala, Sweden. In that particular latitude chicory flower heads opened at 5 A.M. and closed at 10 A.M.

CHICORY

The whole plant is like a rollicking great dandelion and, indeed, it is distantly related to the dandelion, being of the same family group, the *Compositae*. Consequently chicory is used in much the same way. Even its properties are similar to those of the dandelion whose actions are stimulating to both the liver and kidneys and are also slightly laxative. Chicory, too, is found all over Europe and, from the time of the first civilizations, has always contributed to man's diet. The Greek philosopher-botanist Theophrastus referred to the uses of "Cichorium," as did at least three distinguished Romans—Horace, Ovid, and Pliny. It has been a popular vegetable and salad plant from classical times.

Chicory's roots, when grown in good soil so that they become fat and fleshy, have had a long and successful career as a tasty vegetable served with butter. And in modern times they, like the dandelion's roots, have been roasted and ground for mixing with coffee.

Chicory is a weed to be enjoyed, but not to be taken too greedily because continued use upsets the digestion and can affect the eyes. However, a decoction (boiling down) of 1 ounce of the root boiled in 1 quart of water until the liquid is reduced to $1\frac{1}{4}$ pints has mitigated jaundice, liver upsets, gravel (calcium deposits in the bladder or kidneys), gout, and rheumatism. And when used to relieve these disorders, it should be taken freely. The fresh plant, too, is effective against them. Here the formula is 1 ounce of the fresh chicory herb to $1\frac{1}{4}$ pints of boiling water (see page 33). Besides being an excellent tisane, fresh chicory prepared in this same ratio makes a splendid lotion for bathing skin eruptions, especially those caused by gout.

And a water distilled from chicory flowers was used long ago to bathe inflamed eyes.

It is interesting that the confection "Violet Plates," much relished in the days of King Charles II of England, was made from violet and chicory flowers, pounded with honey or sugar. Such flower conserves dating from classical times remained fashionable delicacies for many centuries, in both Europe and America. They were eaten as sweetmeats, placed on dining tables to accompany meat dishes, and given to people suffering from fatigue or headache.

The Clovers

THE CLOVERS: White clover, Dutch clover, honeysuckle, honeysuck, bee-bread, bobby roses, shamrock, three-leaved grass, and claver are among the numerous popular names for this fragrant wild plant. Nicholas Culpeper, the seventeenth-century physician who did so much to disseminate the medical lore of his day to his less-knowledgeable colleagues, wrote about this plant: "It is so well known, especially by the name of honeysuckles, white and red, that I need not describe them." He continued, "They grow almost everywhere in this land." Native to Britain, the white and red clovers range throughout the British Isles, and over Europe as well. They are at home, too, in most of Asia and northern Africa. And they have been introduced into most other lands, notably southern Africa and the North and South American continents, as crop plants.

These honey-laden beeplants were the "clavers" of the Middle Ages and Tudor times. As such, they gave their name to the places where they grew abundantly—for instance, Clavering in Essex, Claverdon in Warwickshire, and Claverton in Cheshire. The Anglo-Saxons spelled it *cloeferwort*. There is a tradition that this name comes from the Latin word *clava,* meaning "club" or "cudgel," and so refers to the plant's three leaflets. For the most famous cudgel in ancient times was the three-knotted club of Hercules, and this association still survives in the three-leafed "clubs" of our playing cards. The three leaflets are characteristic of these plants, bringing luck. But when

WHITE CLOVER

49

clovers are found with four leaflets they bring still more luck (as immortalized in the popular song of the late 1940's). And all the leaves are ancient charms against witches and any other evil.

The white clover is called "Dutch" because it was first recognized in Holland as a valuable agricultural crop. It took British farmers at least a century longer to realize its worth. And when they did, they had to import great quantities of the seed from Holland.

The round clusters of clover flowers, the "bobby roses," are erect in their young, bee-enticing days. But when their pollination is completed, they droop and fade into limp, brown coverings for the developing seed pods.

When all the grass is burnt with summer's heat, the white clover's leaves retain their beautiful green. This is the plant to use for lawns, which you want kept lush and verdant in times of drought. The clovers' roots hold tiny sacs of nitrogen which regale the grasses around them so that they too are fed and stimulated. White clover spreads rapidly to form the desirable thick carpet. One little seedling can cover 10 square feet in a summer's traveling.

The genus name of the clovers is *Trifolium,* meaning "three-leaf" (our modern English word "trefoil" still means any group or thing composed of three connected or closely related parts). And the white clover's species name is *repens*, which describes its creeping growth (in France, it is popularly called *trèfle rampant*). The Trifoliums are members of the same large family as the broom, vetch, sweet pea, and other plants with butterflylike flowers: the *Papilionaceae*. But the clovers' blossoms have tiny wings.

The red clover is a purplish-rose-flowered species whose

botanical name is *Trifolium pratense*. *Pratense* means "growing in meadows." Throughout English-speaking lands this little plant is affectionately referred to as "clover rose," "sugar-bosses," "honeysuckle," "honeysuck," "cowcloos," "lady's posies," "claver," and "red-meadow clover." Although it is native to Britain, it was not introduced into that nation's agriculture until 1645. And for this introduction it was given the more impressive name "marl grass."

Unlike white clover, the red species does not creep. It grows up to 2 feet tall from its several rather lax stems, all of which spring from a single root. Its flowers and leaves are much larger than those of the white clover. Both types have in their roots rich stores of nitrogen. These, along with other worthwhile constituents in their foliage and flowers, make the clover valuable plants in the compost heap. Further, red clover makes an excellent green manure, either grown and dug whole into the soil or cut and laid down as a weed-suppressing mulch. Either way, it will enrich your ground. (A mulch is any covering that is spread upon the ground to protect plant roots from heat, cold, or drought. It may be fabricated from various substances: humus, straw, paper, leaves, sawdust, ground weeds, or a mixture of all these.)

As a medicinal plant, too, the clovers have their virtues. They contain sodium, the mineral that reduces acidity and helps the assimilation of iron in the body (which is sometimes a difficulty). As a side benefit, the texture of both the fingernails and toenails will improve, for it is usually acidity that causes ugly humped or ridgy nails (and thus gives a clue to one's friends and colleagues that the body is not truly functioning as it ought).

The clovers also aid the kidneys and prevent catarrh. (See page 57.) The flowers and leaves make a good, gentle tea that soothes the nervous system, reduces flatulence (intestinal gas), and relieves bronchial coughs. Indeed, clover tea is an old and valued remedy for easing the strain of whooping cough.

This pleasant tea is made by pouring $1\frac{1}{4}$ pints of boiling water over 1 ounce of the plant (see page 33). Both flowers and leaves should be included.

The red and white clovers should both be enjoyed as a good country wine. As it is unlikely that there will be enough of the honeyed blooms in a garden to make this, it is worth the effort of collecting them from any good clover-growing site.

CLOVER WINE

5 quarts of flowers, red or white or both	5 quarts water
3 lemons	2 oranges
3 pounds, best granulated sugar	1 ounce yeast

Boil the sugar and water for a few minutes to make a light syrup, then allow it to cool. When it is lukewarm, take out a coffeecupful and crumble the yeast in. Stir it a little and let the yeast rise until it makes a creamy liquid. Meanwhile put the clover flowers along with the thin yellow peel of the fruits (no white pith) and their juice, into the fermenting vessel. Pour in the cooled syrup and the cupful of creamed yeast. Cover the vessel with a folded cotton cloth and leave it in a warm room for five days. Stir it twice daily with a wooden spoon. Then proceed with Stage 2 (detailed on page 36).

RED CLOVER

Couch Grass

COUCH GRASS, also known as twitch grass, quick grass, scrutch grass, and witch grass, is cosmopolitan, at home and flourishing all over North America, Europe, and northern Asia. It travels as suavely around Australia as it does over South America. It likes loose ground where it can proceed with its creeping rhizomes near the surface. (A rhizome is an underground stem that performs many of the functions of a root. A rhizome is often thick or humped because its plant deposits so much of its reserve food material there. Rhizomes differ from true roots by the presence of buds and scalelike leaves at the joints.) These underground stems give off side branches with bracelets about an inch apart. The bracelets are covered with ginger-colored, elongated hairs, and from these bracelets the new leaf buds and roots arise. If cut by a gardening tool, the couch grass therefore does not die, but becomes several plants instead of one.

The couch grass's rhizome advances with pointed, ivory-colored tips like lances, which force their way through any obstacle such as potatoes and are tough enough to penetrate even tree roots. Couch grass forms so close and strong a network that, away from the garden, it serves the useful purpose of binding the dunes on sandy seashores almost as efficiently as any other of the special grasses used for this preservation.

The name "couch" does not refer to the mattresslike

COUCH GRASS

webbing of the roots, which in itself could be a good enough reason. It is supposed to have survived from the Anglo-Saxon *civice,* meaning "vivacious." This Old English term was applied to the plant because of its vitality and endurance. And herbalists of all eras have maintained that it is able to endow those who use it with these virtues.

"Dog's grass" is another name bestowed on this weed because sickly dogs—and cats, too—seek it to cure their illnesses. In fact, if couch grass is available they eat it regularly to keep themselves fit and healthy. Nicholas Culpeper, after describing this grass, wrote: "If you know it not by this description, watch the dogs when they are sick, and they will quickly lead you to it."

This weed's botanical name, *Agropyron repens,* is less imaginative than the popular ones. It means "field and wheat and creeping." Whatever else you may call it, if this weed is in your garden, it is an herb of importance. Assessing its medical value, Culpeper said " . . . 'tis a remedy against all diseases coming of stopping, and such are half those that are incident to the body of man; and although a gardener be of another opinion, yet a physician holds half an acre of them to be worth five acres of carrots twice told over."

"Twitch" or couch grass is a rich source of potassium, silica, chlorine, and other desirable mineral nutrients, with a special carbohydrate and beneficial sugar. You can see, then, why it is so distressing to think of the countless fires that have been kindled to burn its long, wiry roots after they have been laboriously removed from gardens. Its constituents should make it a boon to any gardener with an ache or twinge, and to his plants. Herbalists sell and use the benevolent, sweet-tasting roots to relieve rheumatism, gout, gravel, kidney disorders, and catarrhal diseases of the bladder. (Catarrhal inflammations are characterized by congestion and swelling of a tissue. Their most easily recognized symptom, however, is a change in the quantity and quality of the diseased tissue's secretions.) Moreover, they claim that the tea infused from couch-grass roots, when taken faithfully and in adequate amounts, is a safe cure for the troublesome infection cystitis (another bladder disease).

Before starting the infusion, clean the roots and free them of their whiskery hairs. Now cut the roots into short pieces and proceed as you would in making any other tisane (see page 33), the ratio being 1 ounce of couch-grass roots to $1\frac{1}{4}$ pints of boiling water. Be sure that the pot is covered so that the element-laden steam cannot escape. This infusion may be taken freely in wineglassful doses. It is not unpleasant. But since it lacks any particular taste, flavoring it with lemon and a little honey will make it more tempting. It is remarkably effective when taken regularly.

The health-giving qualities of couch grass apply equally to the garden. The tea gives its virtues to plants as a liquid feed. Or the roots can be made to donate their stores of nutrients to the compost heap. For this use, though, be careful that enough heat has been generated in the rotting pile to destroy the roots' chances of surviving. (See page 15 for directions on how to construct a compost heap that will create and retain sufficient heat.)

Compost containing quantities of couch grass is especially necessary to replenish the soil where this weed has colonized. Curiously, it tends to discourage further outbreaks of itself when the decomposed weeds are applied in generous, thick mulches at least twice a growing season.

In Continental Europe, the couch-grass story is less clouded by the smoke of bonfires than it is in Britain. There it is recognized as a wholesome, health-giving food for horses and cattle. In Italy, in fact, the roots are painstakingly harvested and then sold in the markets. In France, too, there is a constant demand for these roots, as the French have a keen appreciation of the tisane that can be infused from them.

America shares in the Anglo-Saxon disdain for couch grass. For although this herb can be pulled out of many American gardens by the armful, its commercial outlet seems limited to highly specialized pharmacies. With macrobiotic foods winning more converts each month, however, and with more and more Americans insisting upon organically fed beef and poultry, it is to be hoped that people will soon learn to take advantage of this common garden weed and its health-giving properties.

Dandelion

DANDELION is a naughty weed, but an excellent culinary and medicinal herb. It has acquired a certain universal fame as a "potty" herb, as many of its popular names suggest—"pee-a-bed"; "wet-a-bed"; and in France, *pissen-lit*. The plant contains elements that healthily stimulate man's whole system: bloodstream, liver, digestive organs, and especially the kidneys and bladder. So if it is taken too greedily the effect could be inconvenient and childish.

The dandelion's flowers make it easily recognizable as a member of the daisy tribe, the *Compositae* family. And all the members of this large group are notable for their powerful secretions.

As a garden weed, the dandelion, like the nettle, absorbs about three times as much iron from the soil as is extracted by any other plant. It is a miser, too, for copper and for anything else worthwhile in soil nutrients that it can lay its roots to. Above ground, its beautiful, round, flat flowers that resemble heraldic suns provide a rich pollen food and creamy nectar to honeybees and the wild bees so necessary for pollinating garden crops. On the debit side, however, the dandelion, like some fruits, exhales a breath charged with ethylene gas (see page 21) which hinders the growth of its plant neighbors. Moreover, it depletes the soil until, like the buttercup, it has stunted all the cultivated plants in its vicinity, causing them to produce premature, pygmy fruits and creating disappointment.

The thieving dandelion is acceptable to other plants only when it has been composted—that is, rotted down and disintegrated—so that the usually victimized plants can avail themselves of its hoard of iron, copper, and other valuable elements. Or it can be made into liquid fertilizer and folia feed (see page 32) to remedy other plants' deficiencies (which it has all too often caused).

The dandelion also remedies human deficiencies (in these cases, it is not, of course, the villain). For it can be the best source of copper in our diet. Moreover, it provides iron and constituents such as the bitter taraxacin, inulin (resembling starch), and potash. These last three are contained in its milky juice and have their particular medicinal values. Being nonpoisonous, the plant is harmless and entirely beneficial to humans.

Although the people of the dark and twilight ages could not possibly know the scientific reasons why the dandelion healed, its cures had already been experienced for many centuries before they were recorded by Arabian physicians of the tenth century. In England, there survives from Tudor times a household book that includes a fascinating list of medicinal, cordial, and toilet waters to be regularly infused for the noble's family use. "Water of Tantelyon" is among them.

Tea made from dandelion roots or leaves (see directions on page 33) is of great assistance in relieving disorders of a bilious or dropsical nature. It is also a mild laxative. Further, it aids weak digestions and helps to combat anemia. The dandelion has an ancient reputation for helping to clear gravel and for dispersing skin eruptions. A tea made by decocting 2 ounces of the root or the leaves in $1\frac{1}{4}$ quarts of water until the liquid is boiled down to $1\frac{1}{4}$

DANDELION

pints (or 20 ounces) is highly effective against eczema, scurvy, and all such stubborn skin complaints. This infusion should be taken in wineglassful doses every 3 hours.

Indeed, I have known chronic cases of eczema to be cured completely in just a few weeks when the sufferer began a faithful regimen of drinking dandelion tea mixed with ground elder, in the above doses. Phthisis, a wasting disease of the lungs, is also treated with dandelion tea. As a treatment against this infliction, mix it with ground ivy.

The popular name "dandelion" is a corruption of the French *dent de lion* which, in its turn, derives from the Latin phrase *dens leonis*. But no authority can definitively guide us as to which part of the plant was likened to the lion's tooth. Some say it was the golden petals that were thought to resemble the gilded teeth of heraldic lions. Others maintain that the name is an allusion to the long white taproot. The most likely explanation for the semantic association, however, can be found in a report of a fifteenth-century surgeon. He was so impressed with this plant's ability to overcome certain ailments that he said it was as strong and powerful as a lion's tooth.

The plant's botanical name, *Taraxacum officinale,* filtered down through medieval Latin. Originally, it had a Persian name meaning "bitter potherb sold in shops." This ancient and well-liked culinary herb can supply us with not only its valuable minerals but with greater amounts of vitamins C and A than almost any other vegetable or fruit. Therefore, it is surprising that more American gardeners do not pounce on the sturdy herb and carry it away to the kitchen instead of to the refuse heap. And, in addition to being a fantastic nutrient storehouse, the common dandelion will provide a wide variety of appetizing dishes to any gardener enterprising enough to turn to his own advantage the well-nourished, juicy specimens that so often make flourishing "pests" of themselves in flower beds and borders. All parts of the weed have their long-established uses which should be exploited in the kitchen as they once used to be. In many an old kitchen garden of palace, manor, rectory, and cottage, rows of dandelions were bred to giant size, then manured and pampered to be served at table (some to be blanched like chicory). When splendid salads were appreciated, dandelion's bitter leaves, shredded or chopped roots, and sweet, tangy flowers were all highly prized ingredients.

Today in France these plants are commercially grown to be sold in markets. The tender young leaves are usually mingled with other vegetables to vary their flavors. Or sometimes they are used to add piquancy to salads, as do the roots. The leaves taste somewhat like those of the endive plant.

Salade de pissenlit, a little salad or side salad to be served with a rich meat dish, is made from young and tender dandelion leaves mixed thoroughly with a light dressing of olive oil and a squeeze of lemon juice. This is garnished with a sprinkling of finely chopped chives, parsley, garlic, or borage. This popular French salad is even more delicious when served, as in their sophisticated restaurants, as *pissenlit au lard.* For this variation on the traditional salad, the chef begins with pickled bacon or pork which he blanches by plunging it first into scalding water and then into cold. The blanched meat is then trimmed of fat and cut into small pieces. The tidbits are fried until crisp and dry and are then served *immediately* on a raw dandelion salad that has already been arranged on a piping hot plate. A light dressing composed of vinegar plus a little oil or bacon fat and a dash of salt and pepper completes this gourmet dish.

As a vegetable, the dandelion is delightful if cooked with care. Wash the tender young leaves and place them in a pan without shaking off the water. Add a large dab of butter and a light seasoning of salt and pepper. Cook slowly until the leaves are tender. Turn them occasionally to prevent their burning and to ensure that all the leaves are permeated with the butter. Now strain the herbs and serve them hot with a squeeze of lemon juice and a sprinkling of chopped chives or parsley.

Dandelion leaves are a happy accompaniment to spinach, but they should be partly cooked before the spinach is put on the stove because they take longer than spinach. Prepare the young dandelion leaves as described above. When they are half done, add your wet spinach leaves with a dab of butter. Strain the greens and serve hot with more butter and a squeeze of lemon juice.

Dandelion coffee is made from the roots of the plant and is so beneficial to human organs that it is sold in superior stores and health-food shops. Moreover, it is served as an after-dinner beverage in vegetarian restaurants. Although hostesses will never vie with one another to serve it at their dinner parties, dandelion coffee is a wholesome brew that can be perfectly appropriate at other, less formal occasions. It tastes like weak coffee, but is kinder to delicate stomachs than the "real stuff." Moreover, while imparting the vast vitamin and mineral gifts which "real" coffee lacks, it is entirely free of troublesome caffeine. And dandelion coffee is also an effective sleep-inducing nightcap that even children and invalids may enjoy.

To make it, clean the roots and dry them thoroughly. Now roast them to coffee color in a cool oven. They may be stored for a short time in airtight cans or jars, to be freshly ground just before you brew this beverage for your family or friends.

Dandelion Beer

Dandelion beer, apart from being a very popular country tipple, was the drink most favored in the past by workers in British iron foundries and potteries. It is a refreshing and enjoyable drink. And while you are still savoring the taste, the herb will be at work clearing the kidneys and bladder. Dandelion beer is also particularly good at relieving indigestion and upset stomachs. To make it, the *entire* plant must be dug up from the ground. The following recipe is well worth the effort involved and the product will add further zest to your spring season:

$\frac{1}{2}$ pound young dandelion plants

1 ounce yeast

1 pound Demerara sugar (a special raw cane sugar having yellowish-brown crystals)

1 lemon

5 quarts water

1 ounce cream of tartar

$\frac{1}{2}$ ounce bruised ginger root

Put the sugar and cream of tartar in the vessel that you will use to ferment the beer. Pound the ginger root thoroughly so that it is well bruised. Now turn to the plants: Wash them and remove their hairy roots, being careful not to break the main taproots. Place the washed plants in a pan along with the bruised ginger root and some lemon rind (no white pith) and the water. Boil the mixture for 10 minutes. Now strain out the solids and pour the liquid over the sugar and cream of tartar in your fermenting vessel. Stir until the sugar is dissolved. When the liquid is lukewarm, add the yeast and the lemon juice. Leave the vessel, covered with a folded cloth, in a warm room for three days. Strain out all the sediment and bottle the final liquid in clean glass bottles with screw-top caps. (An empty, sterilized soda bottle with a twist-on cap would be excellent for this purpose.) Now store the filled bottles on their sides. This beer will be ready to drink in about a week. You can tell when the time is ripe, because the beer will hiss as you loosen the cap. Take full advantage of your brew, for it does not keep very long.

Dandelion Wines

A well-made dandelion wine can be as pleasurable as many an expensive foreign wine. Moreover, it is gratifying to know that while you are enjoying this country brew, it is actually good for your health. The wines are fermented from the golden, nectar-rich flower petals. No greenery must come into it as the greenery stops the fermentation and spoils the delicate flavor that should be the wine's attraction. The flowers must be gathered on a dry day and after the dew has left them. The first recipe makes a light, dry, sherrylike wine.

Dandelion Wine 1 (Dry)

2½ quarts dandelion petals

3 pounds, best granulated sugar

2 lemons

5 quarts water (boil)

2 oranges

1 ounce yeast

Clean the dandelion petals and put them into a bowl or plastic bucket that will hold more than 5 quarts. Now, pour all of your boiling water over them and stir with a wooden spoon. Cover the vessel and leave it for two or three days, stirring daily. Then transfer the contents into a large pot. Add thinly peeled rinds of the fruit (no white pith) and bring to a boil. Turn down the heat and simmer for 10 minutes. Now put the sugar into a fermenting vessel and strain the boiled mixture over it through several thicknesses of cheesecloth or muslin. Or one layer of closely woven cotton may be used. When the strained liquor is lukewarm, add the juice of the fruits and stir in the yeast. Leave the brew to ferment in a warm room for two or three weeks, then proceed with Stage 2 (see page 36). This wine may be drunk after eight months' maturing, but it improves when kept longer.

Dandelion Wine 2 (Sweet)

This recipe makes a sweet wine that must be kept for at least a year before it can be drunk.

3¾ quarts petals

3½ pounds Demerara sugar

½ pound large raisins

1 lemon

5 quarts water (boil)

½ ounce bruised ginger root

1 orange

1 ounce yeast

Clean the petals and put them into a bowl or plastic bucket. Pour the gallon and a quarter of boiling water over them. Cover this solution with a folded cotton cloth and leave for three days, stirring several times daily. Now strain it into a pot. *Then* add the sugar, the thin yellow peel (no white pith) of the fruits, and the ginger root which should be well pounded (to bruise it). Bring this mixture to a boil and then simmer it for 30 minutes, from time to time adding more boiling water to make up the original 5 quarts as they evaporate into steam. Allow your brew to cool a little, then strain out all the solids through several layers of muslin or cheesecloth. The liquid, of course, seeps straight into the fermenting vessel. Add the chopped raisins and the fruit juice immediately, and when the liquor is lukewarm put in the yeast and stir. Cover snugly with a folded cotton cloth and leave the solution to ferment in a warm room for two or three weeks. Then proceed with Stage 2 (see page 36).

Day Lily

DAY LILY, this plant is popularly called because of the limited life of its lovely flowers. Its botanical name, *Hemerocallis,* means the same fleeting pleasure from the Greek *hemero,* "a day," and *kallos,* "beauty." It is an entirely decorative plant growing like some robust iris but bearing lily flowers of rich colors, according to its many varieties and hybrids. After the day's display, evening's fading blooms are so quickly followed the next morning by newly opened buds that their transience is usually unnoticed. As a garden plant it forms a generous clump of erect, fresh green leaves over a long period of time and, in its season, is crowned with a mass of gorgeous heads of flowers. The plant is of the lily family, *Liliaceae,* and, in shape, its trumpet blooms are typical.

The day lily is a plant of more than ordinary stamina, ease of culture, and freedom from disease. It has no preferences for types of soil or of temperature and thrives equally well in the sands of Florida, the red clay of Alabama, or the loam of Iowa. New England's acid soil merely deepens the color of the flowers compared with those produced in the alkaline areas of Texas. The day lily is as happy in the sub-zero temperatures of Canada as it is in the mild climate of California or the high temperatures of Arizona. Its seeds are easily raised, and its roots have the tough constitution of horseradish so that they multiply readily. Thus this plant, which began in China, Siberia, and Japan and was brought to England only as late as 1596, has distributed itself over most of central and southern Europe. By today it is a wild plant that has achieved for itself the rating of a weed almost throughout Europe and America.

In its native lands, the edible day lily provides some pleasant foods, especially when taken in conjunction with pork and soy sauce. So its roots, buds, and flowers could with all good reason claim their places in any Western menu—and would certainly be enjoyed.

Dig up a spadeful of root from a clump and remove the small tubers that nestle underneath. If you have raided a garden colony the older tubers should be replanted on another site, perhaps in the vegetable plot where they will thrive and produce more of the little vegetable. These tiny tubers are sweet to taste, having a flavor resembling that of broad beans with a background of whole sweet corn. Moreover, they are available throughout the year so long as the ground is not frozen. The buds and flowers are culinary pleasures whether fresh or dried. For all these reasons, the plant is a more permanent asset than any other vegetable tenant of the plot.

On the next pages you will find just a few of the ways in which you can use day lilies to embellish your family's diet.

SALAD: Cold cooked tubers make an excellent salad: Mix them with chopped parsley, savory, and a little finely chopped onion or chives. Now rub the bowl with garlic and moisten the entire medley with French dressing or mayonnaise.

Uncooked, the fresh crisp tubers are delicious when eaten like radishes. Or they can go into a salad, either whole or coarsely chopped.

70   **Day Lily**

DAY LILY

71

HORS D'OEUVRES: The raw tubers are marvelous served with an herb butter. To make this add to $\frac{1}{2}$ teacupful of creamed butter, $\frac{1}{2}$ tablespoonful of finely chopped or minced parsley, and $1\frac{1}{2}$ tablespoonfuls of chopped savory. Mix together with a teaspoonful of lemon juice and seasoning to taste. A few chopped chives may be added with advantage.

A THICK TUBER SOUP to serve four persons. You will need the following ingredients—

Water: $1\frac{1}{2}$ quarts	Carrots: 2
Small shallots: 3	Savory herbs and parsley:
Celery: 1 good stick	$\frac{1}{2}$ ounce each
Butter: 2 ounces	Sugar: 1 lump
Day-lily tubers: 2 pounds	Eggs: 3 yolks only

Boil the water and then toss most of the tubers into it, along with a dash of salt and pepper (to taste) and the other vegetables. Keep boiling very gently for $1\frac{1}{2}$ hours.

Press the vegetables through a sieve, keeping aside the liquid. Now mash them to obtain a purée. Put the purée into a saucepan with the 2 ounces of butter and the remaining uncooked tubers. Add the sugar lump and, little by little, stir the liquid in. Boil this blend again for 15 minutes. Finally, add the 3 egg yolks, well-beaten, and serve the soup with a few croutons that have been lightly fried in butter. A few flowers—it is unimportant whether they are newly opened, faded, or dried—should be added to this, or any other, soup during the last 15 minutes of cooking.

THE BUDS as a vegetable: Boil the green buds (no stalks) for a few minutes and serve them with the herb butter (See recipe for hors d'oeuvres, given above).

A SAVORY DISH: Remove the stalks and dip the buds into a good batter and fry crisp. To make the batter, allow 1 ounce of melted butter to 6 ounces of flour, a good pinch of salt, and the yolk of an egg. Add a dessertspoonful of finely chopped or minced herbs, then mix together with a wooden spoon, gradually adding a teacupful of tepid water. Mix until creamy, then let the batter stand for an hour. While you are waiting, you can whip the egg white lightly until it is stiff. Now, just before you are ready to use the batter, gently fold in the frothy egg white.

A SWEET DISH: Make a batter according to the Process given above (See recipe for savory dish). But instead of using salt, substitute a generous pinch of sugar. And instead of the herbs, use a little grated lemon or orange peel. Now dip the stalkless buds into your batter. Fry and serve with white sugar.

SWEET FRITTERS: Dip each day-lily flower into a *plain* batter and fry all at once in sizzling fat. Serve hot, sprinkled with white sugar. Luscious!

Day-lily buds are a delightful addition to any soup or stew and they may be dried for winter use. The flowers, too, give a rich flavor and will, moreover, add a thickness to your soups, stews, and casseroles. Remember that both buds and flowers should be added during the final 15 minutes of cooking.

The flowers can be used fresh, faded, or after they have been dried for storing. To dry the flowers and buds, place them on newspaper in a dry, airy room away from sunshine (which ruins the flavor). Keep turning them until they are quite dry—it will take about two weeks—then store them in sterilized jars that have screw-on lids. Before using, restore these buds and flowers by soaking them in plain water for a little while. A great many blooms and buds can be gathered from just one foray on the colonies of the wild day lily, and it is well worth a trip into the country to gather them.

The food value of this plant is unquestionable. And the roots of *Hemerocallis fulva,* the dark-orange-flowered type, have long been used in herbal remedies for the treatment of ulcers and tumors.

Dead Nettles

DEAD NETTLES is a name that encompasses the henbit, red dead nettle, white dead nettle, and yellow dead nettle plants, all four of which are more popularly known in America as "henbit." They are entitled to the strangely favorable label "dead" because in this case it distinguishes them from the "true" or stinging nettle whose leaves their own resemble. Yet *none* of the dead nettles are in any way related to the stinging nettles. For all four are members of the large *Labiatae* family. (Stinging nettles, as we shall see later on, belong to an entirely different family, the *Urticaceae*.) This means that all our dead nettles have characteristic flowers with pouting lips and stems that are square. The large *Labiatae* family includes many other plants, all wholly unlike the stinging nettles. For instance, our cherished aromatic herbs lavender, rosemary, mint, and thyme are all members.

The henbit—an entirely separate weed that is so widely distributed as to force its name onto all other types of dead nettles in America—most closely resembles the red dead nettle. Indeed, it might sometimes seem that their points of difference could concern only botanist-gardeners. However, bees are involved—and so are we, if we would know our weedy friends. Both the henbit and the red dead nettle are members of the *Lamium* genus. This Latin name comes from the Greek word for "throat" or "gullet" and it refers to the specially long tubular corollas of the characteristically labiate (lipped) flowers. The two weeds can be thought of as cousins.

The henbit is *Lamium amplexicaule*. Its species name means "stem-embracing," as its upper leaves are stalkless. It prefers a light soil where it can enjoy a long, independent, and fruitful life. For although it is an annual, it can be found flowering almost throughout the year. Certainly, in mild winters it continues to flaunt its rose-colored blooms that are mainly for show and do nothing to propagate the species. It has other flowers however, inconspicuous ones that do not open but self-pollinate the seeds that nestle safely inside. So henbit does not rely on bees or any other insect, but instead gets along very well without them. Its average seed production per plant reaches about a thousand, but only a few offspring survive. Henbit is not gregarious and never appears in abundant masses.

Except in the extreme north, this wild plant ranges all over Europe and down to the Azores and the Canary Islands. It is common in Palestine, also in Persia, and it has become naturalized in North America. Authorities studying plant affinities say that henbit is so helpful and encouraging to growing vegetables that a few of them should be placed among potatoes and other crops in the kitchen garden. For this purpose we ought to know how to distinguish the more slender and graceful henbit from the sturdier, more prolific, and less helpful red dead nettle. Unlike this plant, henbit's corolla tubes are not hidden by the upper leaves and they do not have the same ring of hairs. Henbit's leaves are rounded, rather heart-shaped, and have deeply cut edges. Those of the red dead nettle are tinged with purple and often clothed with silky hairs.

HENBIT AND RED DEAD NETTLE

The red dead nettle is *Lamium purpureum*. Its species name means purple. It, too, is an annual: "perishing every year; the whole plant hath a strong scent, but not stinking," wrote Culpeper. He also remarked, "To put a gloss upon their practice, the physicians call an herb (which country people vulgarly know by the name of dead nettle) archangel: whether they favour more of superstition or folly, I leave to the judicious reader."

The red dead nettle originated as a wild plant in the mountainous regions of southern Europe and developed the energetic capacity of flowering and fruiting for eight months of the year, even in cool, damp climates. It has rose-purple blooms very like those of henbit, but with a ring of purple hairs at the base of the corolla. It does not entirely depend on bees for pollination. It too can manage alone and can produce large colonies. For if undisturbed, its prostrate shoots will root at the joints in the colder months of the year.

It is interesting that in the north the red dead nettle seems to date from the Roman occupation of Britain. Once imported by the Roman legions, it naturalized itself as a wild plant and a native medicinal herb. Today it is a common garden weed in both Britain and America.

The yellow dead nettle, known as the "weaselsnout," was once classed as *Lamium galeobdolon*. But for structural reasons botanists have given it a separate genus, and it is now *Galeobdolon luteum*. This name is not a happy choice, as it means "weasel and stench" and condemns this pretty woodland plant to be known all over the world for only the unpleasant smell of its crushed leaves and stems. This seems all the more unfair when we consider that many a nastier-smelling plant has a nicer botanical name. The

WHITE DEAD NETTLE

79

attractive flowers are a lovely yellow, and this color gives the plant its species name. As a garden weed, this perennial is somewhat scarce except in wooded areas. However, it can be readily found in the forests of Europe, including those of northern Russia.

The white dead nettle (*Lamium album*) is also a perennial. It is a very frequent weed in Britain, as its brittle roots are easily broken to form new plants. And its abundance in hedges, along roadsides, and in waste places makes it a constant visitor to gardens. Its seeds are pollinated by long-tongued, honey-loving insects, mainly bumblebees whose velvet behinds can be seen wriggling from almost every delightful greenish-white flower. This frequent association gives the white dead nettle two of its popular names, "bee nettle" and "honey flower." It is also called "Adam and Eve" because if one holds its blossom upside down, the black and gold stamens lying side by side are like two sleeping people in a translucent silken tent.

Both the white dead nettle and its relation, the black horehound (a variety of European mint), are among the rare plants that, as a means of protecting themselves, imitate another, better equipped plant that is quite unrelated to them. It is most usual to find horehound and the white dead nettle growing and mingling with stinging nettles; the plants are so alike in foliage that unless you know your nettles, they can deceive you. The flowers, however, are very different. Horehound, stinging nettles, and white dead nettles are three natural companions, although their evolved similarity and behavior is a botanical curiosity.

All the dead nettles contain a useful supply of elements to enrich the compost heap. It follows, then, that they are also valuable medicines for the practicing herbalist. Tea infused from them (see page 33) and sweetened with pure honey is a handy domestic remedy for chill. The plants can also be boiled and eaten as potherbs. (A potherb is any herb that is boiled before being eaten, but we also apply this term to parsley, thyme, bay leaf, and marjoram when they are used in the form of a bouquet to flavor stews, sauces, and the like.)

To use dead nettles as a vegetable, gather the young, tender flowering-tips and wash them. Then put the wet leaves into a pan with no more water, but with a good dab of butter or margarine. Cook them gently, turning and mixing them occasionally to avoid burning. Meanwhile, season lightly with salt and pepper. Strain them when tender and serve hot with butter. A tastier mixture is made by adding some chopped chives or spring onions.

One final word about these plants: In Britain all four are most often referred to by the rather poetic name "archangel."

Feverfew

FEVERFEW, featherfew, or flirtwort is properly called *Chrysanthemum parthenium* and is a member of the daisy-flowered family, *Compositae*. The name "feverfew" is a corruption of "febrifuge," from its fever-lessening properties.

The herb probably originated in southeastern Europe, but it has been transported and cultivated for many centuries. In this era, it has escaped into the countryside and now spreads almost everywhere as a wild plant decorating waysides. At waste places, it may be the last lingering sign of some ancient habitation. It was once a plant of consequence which was set around dwellings in the belief that it purified the air and kept disease at bay. It also served as a medicine to cool feverishness, to quiet palpitations, and to calm nervousness and lift up low spirits.

Culpeper recommended feverfew for women who had just given birth, "to remedy such infirmities as a careless midwife has caused." He also chided lazy women who had given birth during the winter months and were now grumbling at the unavailability of the herb. For a beneficial syrup could have been made of feverfew the previous summer, he reminds them.

A decoction of the weed's flowers in wine, made more palatable by a dash of nutmeg, was a Tudor remedy for many other of women's ailments. And the powdered

FEVERFEW

herb, dissolved in wine and mixed with honey and a little vinegar, served to relieve vertigo (dizziness and confusion of the mind) in both sexes.

A very ancient belief, which retains much truth, is that the infusion of feverfew's flowers had an aspirinlike sedative effect that would reduce any distressing sensitiveness to pain in a very nervous subject. Moreover, the tisane helps to induce quiet, restful sleep. It also relieves toothache, earache, neuralgia, and some rheumatic pains. Other virtues are the herb's ability to loosen phlegm and to "help those who are short-winded." Herbalists employ it to promote menses—and to expel worms from children.

The infusion that tackles all these ills is made by pouring $1\frac{1}{4}$ pints of boiling water over 1 ounce of the herb, fresh or dried (see page 33) and it is taken frequently when it is cold, in doses of half a teacupful. Dabbed on the skin, this brew is also an insect repellent that discourages gnats and biting flies. (It was once greatly esteemed for combating the nighttime invasion of bugs and fleas.)

Feverfew is a perennial growing about 2 feet tall. In appearance, the plant resembles a camomile and it has some of the same virtues. The numerous small daisylike flowers are borne in a similar flat-topped cluster, but they have flat central discs, not conical ones like those of the camomile. The feathery aromatic foliage may be a delicate green; when cultivated it is usually a golden-green color. A few of the pungent, rather bitter leaves chopped fine are good sprinkled on salads to give a zest to the mixture.

Great Mullein

MULLEIN, great mullein, mullein dock, Our Lady's Flannel, velvet dock—all these are among the familiar names for this handsome, plushy-leaved wilding. In shape and size, the long pointed leaves resemble those of its relative the foxglove, but they are entirely clothed in a thick coat of whitish hairs. These have evolved as an efficient feature for self-preservation: No insect can penetrate the obstruction, and the hairs are so irritating that cattle are seldom tempted to eat the leaves. This "felt" coat also helps by catching and holding moisture so that it can be taken in by the leaves and by lessening evaporation from their surface. Thus it enables the herb to survive even in dry, sunny situations. Mullein is further equipped by small leaves on its tall, furred stem. These drip rain onto the large leaves of the basal rosette that supplies the roots and keeps them moist and cool with its covering spread.

Usually the stem rises about 5 feet, but in good garden soil it can attain a height of 8 feet. And for this achievement it has collected such names as Aaron's, Jupiter's, and Peter's Rod. The stalkless flowers top the stem in a long, crowded steeple. They are a bright sulphur-yellow and measure an inch across, each having five rounded petals that form a short tube at the base. Three of the five stamens are shorter than the other two and these shorter stamens bear a quantity of tiny hairs that are full of sap. Functioning as a "sampling bar" this sap lures insect customers with the promise of the delicious nectar lying easily accessible in the base of the ovary. Mullein's clientele of insects is dominated by various kinds of bees. But our weed is independent. It can, when necessary, produce seeds without their help.

Great mullein is a biennial known to botanists as *Verbascum thapsus*. The Roman scholar Pliny gave the weed its generic name (*Verbascum*) in his writing as a naturalist. Its species name was derived from either the ancient city of Thapsus in Africa (a coastal town in what is now Tunisia) or from the Grecian island Thapsos. The plants belong to the huge family *Scrophulariaceae,* which can claim at least 2,400 different species of very wide distribution. The great mullein grows wild all over Europe, and throughout temperate Asia as far south as the Himalayas. Long ago it earned a widespread reputation as a useful domestic herb. One of its old names, "candle-wick plant," referred to the use of the dried hairs as a reliable tinder that would instantly ignite. In addition, before the introduction of cotton wicks, the dried leaves of the mullein when floated in oil or fat provided lamp wicks. In olden days, its long straight stems were coated with suet (animal fat that, when melted down, forms tallow) to make great candles for burning at funerals and other august ceremonies. For this employment the plant was called "torches" and, also, "Our Lady's Candle."

Great mullein was so important a plant that, as the *herbe de St. Fiacre,* it was dedicated to the seventh-century Irish saint who went to live in France and became the patron saint of gardeners.

Mullein had a great reputation for warding off evil spirits and thwarting witches' spells. According to

GREAT MULLEIN

87

classical writers, it was the unassuming mullein that protected Ulysses against Circe's fearsome power to change anybody into a four-legged beast. (His less-prepared companions were transformed into swine.)

As mullein provided comforting, simple-to-make medications for several ills, it is natural that the settlers emigrating to America should take the herb with them. In its new home it found the growing good, became naturalized, and spread by virtue of its massive seed production. Today it is an abundant weed in the Eastern States.

But mullein should be treated as a weed only when it becomes a nuisance. It is a valuable herb and is grown in most admirable herb gardens. The plant is decorative. Moreover, the roots are confined, not invasive. And because they delve down so far, they drain and ventilate reaches of the soil which shallow-rooted plants cannot attain and thus enhance their shallow-rooted neighbors' growth. This is but one more example of how weeds can work to the advantage of the cultivated plants in one's garden.

This is a weed we can enjoy solely for its appearance, and it is almost as a bonus that it offers curative tisanes. The plant's constituents are entirely benign. The leaves secrete gum, resin, tannin, and a valuable oil. Its flowers contain gum, resin, phosphoric acid, chlorophyll, and a glucoside, as well as mineral salts such as lime, and a volatile oil. The herb yields a soothing mucilage that, astringent and relaxing, acts like a balm on the alimentary canal. (This mucilage is a sticky juice containing carbohydrates and many beneficial plant acids. It is a highly prized ingredient for the making of many commercial medicines.) And because it is slightly sedative and narcotic mullein also is an aid to restful sleep.

The tea is made by infusing 1 ounce of leaves or flowers, either fresh or dried, in $1\frac{1}{4}$ pints of boiling water. Unlike most herbal teas, mullein's *must be strained* when the infusion has cooled, in order to catch the leaf and stamen hairs. Use a fine cheesecloth, muslin, or cotton cloth for this purpose. When frequently taken in wineglassful doses, this tisane will relieve simple diarrhea, catarrhs, and coughs. When it is made with milk, a mullein infusion is a nourishing and soothing medication for pulmonary complaints.

An infusion of mullein flowers taken before breakfast is said to give relief from gout. An old use for the felty leaves was to wear them in the shoes to stimulate circulation, to keep the feet warm, and to discourage chilblains. And homeopaths (see pages 7 and 8) recommend this weed to ease migraine pain.

Mullein leaves are far too hairy to go into salads, but the bald flowers should be used as they are pretty and health-giving.

Ground Ivy

GROUND IVY, also known as alehoof, tunhoof, blue runner, cat's-foot, gill-creep-by-the-ground, hedge-maids, and Creeping Jenny, was taken to America by early English settlers. It was part of their standard stock of household herbs, and these transplanted Englishmen continued its familiar uses. But in the New World it became "Creeping Charlie."

Ground ivy is not so common a weed in British gardens as many other wildings. The exceptions are gardens near the countryside and in areas of the nation where the soil is damp and not too light and sandy. Then it will try to spread its carpet and settle down.

In America, however, this attractive weed does not show such good manners. It is among the most familiar of garden invaders, from Maine to Georgia, and as far west as Colorado. Once it has found a cool, shady place in which to send out its runners, these long tendrily stems readily root and produce a dense persistent carpet. Any lax gardener on the eastern seaboard is likely to find his flower beds pre-empted by this creeping weed. And it is tough enough to infiltrate even rock gardens.

As a European *wild* plant, however, it grows everywhere: on waste ground, along roadsides, and in the thickets that fringe cultivated fields. It especially loves the proximity of oak woods, for forests of these trees will provide nearby ground with the moist, sunless environ-

GROUND IVY

ment in which the ground ivy plant thrives. It is rugged enough to be found even in the Arctic Circle upon occasion.

This perennial has trailing stems with root fibers that penetrate the soil at frequent intervals. By this ingenious means of locomotion, it can quickly cover large areas of ground with its evergreen, rather hairy, heart-shaped, scalloped leaves. The showy, lipped flowers arise in little half circles from the leaf axils, and their color varies through numerous shades of bluish-purple. Some blossoms are dark, others are pale—and sometimes there are pure white ones. When the ground ivy grows on a shaded site, all its leaves are green. On the rare occasions when it takes up residence in a sunny place, its stems and foliage will often glow. And they are very lovely, tinged, as they hug the ground, with crimson and purple.

This carpeting plant's botanical name is now *Glecoma hederacea*. Its present generic name originated from the label given it as a species tag by a first-century Greek physician (his name was Dioscorides, and his writings remained for 1,500 years the definitive authority on botany and the medicinal values of herbs in the Western world). Its current species name, *Hederacea*, means "ivylike." Whether our weed earned this title because it creeps as successfully as "true" ivy or because its leaves suggest those of the true ivy plant, I don't know. Remember, however, that "true" ivy plants are actually climbing, woody vines that belong to the ginseng family. And we recognize true ivies by their clambering growth.

On the other hand, while the ground ivy weed will transform every inch of soil allowed it into a brilliant, decorative carpet, we will never find it twining itself around arbors or mailbox posts. It cannot. Nor will it ever serve as attractive wall coverings on colleges.

At one time, ground ivy's botanical name was *Nepeta glecoma*, and it also bears some resemblance to its erect relative, the *Nepeta cataria*, or catnip plant. But catnip is of course not a weed, but a popular garden herb having several gay, cultivated species. Both catnip and ground ivy belong to the large mint family, the lipped-blossomed *Labiatae* which includes most of our favorite aromatic herbs and many essential medicinal ones. At one time our ground ivy was deemed as useful as the rest of them.

The brewing of ale from grain has been important for thousands of years. The earliest Egyptians, the Greeks, the Romans, and all other early peoples who could boil a potful of water to make some sort of convivial brew considered themselves the more civilized for achieving this knack. It was the German brewers who first discovered the value of hops in their brewing and were growing them for that purpose in the eighth century. But until this acrid plant was introduced into other countries (and it was not allowed in Britain until after the fourteenth century) only wild herbs could be used to flavor the brew. And since of all the greenery in Britain, ground ivy was the most widely chosen seasoning substance, it became the "alehoof," the "tunhoof" (tun meaning, in those days, "to tipple"). Thus, even later it remained, with yarrow and a few other plants, the favored flavoring and clearing agent in home brewing. Of this function Nicholas Culpeper wrote, "It is good to tun up with new drink, for it will clarify it in a night, that it will be fitter to be dranke the next morning; or if any drinke be thick with removing or any other accident, it will do the like in a few hours."

Until a century or so ago, brewing was an ordinary household task, and until the seventeenth century many people considered hops to be dangerous to health. Another of ground ivy's names, "gill," came from the French *guiller* (meaning "to ferment ale"). And since gill also meant a girl, the plant was soon called "hedge-maids."

Gill tea was the ancient all-purpose drink. It is cooling; stimulating; and excellent for relieving coughs, indigestion, and kidney complaints. It is still recommended by herbalists, and they sell ground ivy in a dried form. The tea is infused with 1 ounce of the herb to $1\frac{1}{4}$ pints of boiling water (see page 33). It should be taken in wineglassful doses four times a day. This wild plant was once hawked in the streets of London for making curative tea, and the peddlers of ground ivy had their own specialized "cry" or sales pitch. The cooled tisane is also a lotion for weak, tired, and sore eyes. Combined with yarrow, ground ivy makes an effective poultice for abscesses. And because it is the most potent herb we have against pulmonary complaints, it was once the medicine of hope for consumptives.

Looking down the list of its achievements, from its being "a singular herb for all inward wounds, exulcerated lungs, or other parts," to its curing of gout, sciatica, and jaundice, there appear to be few complaints of the body of man—or of beats—that ground ivy cannot cope with. And according to Graeco-Roman mythology it even cheers away melancholy.

In the garden, ground ivy secretes a useful amount of iron which, along with its other constituents, makes it a welcome addition to the compost heap.

Groundsel

GROUNDSEL. About this weed Nicholas Culpeper wrote, "This herb is Venus' mistress-piece, and is as gallant and universal a medicine for all diseases coming of heat, in what part of the body soever they be as the sun shines upon." (Culpeper hitched his every herb to a planet or star.)

By "Venus' mistress-piece," the eminent herbalist is probably referring to the fact that the little weed was widely regarded in Europe as a love charm. And it is part of medieval Christian folklore that it formed part of the Virgin Mary's bed.

The name "groundsel" descends almost uncorrupted from the early Anglo-Saxons. They called the plant *groundswelge*, meaning "earth-glutton" or "ground devourer." In the north of England it is still "grundy-swallow" and it is a greedy weed anywhere—and almost everywhere. For this plant accompanied even wandering tribes of prehistoric men on their travels and emigrations and ever since the eons of those first harsh rovings, it has settled comfortably in man's every colony. Only in the tropics did the groundsel leave mankind to its own devices. For there the heat proved too much for a plant originating in temperate Europe—even the insatiable groundsel.

Groundsel is an annual of wonderful perseverance. The

plants are in flower and ready to fruit every month of the year, unless they are hidden under deep snow. No gardener stands a chance of permanently getting the better of it. New seeds will arrive from somewhere, somehow—and will do so every day. They sail on the wind, and many settle on garden fences and garage windows. There they roost, unnoticed, until it is too late to stop their seeding. Wipe groundsel out with a hoe and you stir up fresh seeds that, within a few weeks, will be flourishing plants. On poor soil it rushes into seed production as a tiny tot. Only on good land does it take its time to mature, so that the gardener stands a reasonable chance of cutting it down before the seeds are dispatched. But if he fails, each plant can be responsible for one million descendants in a year.

This weed was once grown as a crop, principally as a food for pigs, goats, rabbits, and poultry. Either fresh or dried it was used in summer and winter, and its effects were both wholesome and soothing. For the plant contains a sufficient amount of iron and other mineral constituents to remedy animals' feebleness and nervous disorders. Even children feeding it to pet rabbits that are sick, find that the weed tempts the little invalids to take food and thus eventually recover. Large quantities of groundsel are sold to be enjoyed by canaries and other caged birds. (If you are feeding it to parakeets, be careful of the doses however, as too much groundsel will cause your pet to lose its feathers out of season.)

Apart from its food value for the gardener's pets and poultry, groundsel is a valuable source of iron and other desirable things and therefore should be returned to the soil. It may be buried, for its life span is over once it loses

GROUNDSEL

its first tenuous grip on the soil. And it certainly should be composted if you can find no other uses for this little herb.

For several reasons, herbalists still stock this ancient medicinal plant, and a *very* weak tea infused from the fresh weed (increase the amount of water given in our formula of page 33) is a mild laxative and relieves biliousness (an excess of bile, usually connected with a malfunctioning liver. This discomfort is characterized by headache, dizziness, and constipation). It is also an insurance against scurvy. But a stronger brew is an emetic of gentle persuasion that causes no painful effects, and it is preferable in a domestic emergency to the usual drastic doses of salt water or mustard—especially when it is children who have swallowed poisons. To make an excellent soothing lotion for curing chapped hands and roughened skin, pour some boiling water over a handful of groundsel plants and let the infusion cool. This herb's other uses, such as for killing worms in children, ought to be left to the herbalist.

In a herbal of Tudor times, the description of groundsel says: "The flower of this herbe hath white hair, and when the winde bloweth it away, then it appeareth like a bald-headed man." This agrees with the plant's botanical name, *Senecio vulgaris*, which Pliny gave it. For *senex* is Latin for "old man." And *vulgaris*, meaning "of the people," probably refers to the frequency with which it was found around the dwellings of man. Groundsel is of the *Compositae* family and it has the same attraction as its relation, the chrysanthemum, for the leaf-mining pest, the marguerite fly. This minute tormentor lays its eggs on foliage in spring, and the tracks of the maggots' tunneling inside the leaves are very obvious. Groundsel plants so affected

should be buried deep enough to smother the grubs
before they emerge as mature flies ready to attack other,
cultivated plants. In this, the weed acts as a valuable early
trap. For it can catch and hold, for a short time, thousands
of destructive potential flies.

Although groundsel thrives all over America, it is
especially abundant in the plains region—probably
because, there, the wind has almost unhampered license
to distribute the weed's feathery, seed-filled fruits. *Senecio
aureus* ("golden-haired old man") is another common
American variety.

Horsetail

THE HORSETAIL is often called cat's-tail in English-speaking lands. Nearly two thousand years ago, the Roman naturalist Pliny gave this odd-looking plant its present botanical name, *Equisetum arvense*, which means "horse and bristle of the fields." He thought its general appearance resembled a horse's tail, but the country people of Britain have long likened it to a cat's tail instead. And this name spread to many of the countries that they colonized.

The *arvense* horsetail, with which we as gardeners are concerned, is an almost universal weed that prefers drier ground than some of its near relations. Many horsetails—other species of the vastly interesting *Equisetum* genus—inhabit marshy sites. So, because of its preference for dry locations, our weed is often called the "field horsetail" or "field cat's-tail." Frequently, however, this plant is misnamed "mare's-tail." This is all the more erroneous because "mare's-tail" is the popular name for an aquatic plant that lives in the rich beds of lakes. Mare's-tail, too, has bristly whorls, but it is of the *Hippuris* genus and in no way related to the horsetails. Nevertheless, several centuries ago the two plants were commonly believed to be male and female of the same species, the girls for some reason living in the water, and the boys coming into the garden from neglected fields.

Mare's-tail plants and horsetails have one extraordinary facet in common though: Both belong to genera that are the sole survivors of their respective plant families. For just as the *Hippuris* genus is the only present-day representative of the *Hippuridaceae* family, so the *Equisetum* genus is all that has come down to us from the *Equisetaceae* family. Yet there was a time when the *Equisetaceae* family contained many genera, and all of its mammoth-sized plants contributed a great deal to the coal deposits of our planet during the Carboniferous period during which that family thrived.

For all its exotic history though, the field horsetail remains today nothing but a persistent bane to many a British gardener. In this roosting behavior it is a direct contrast to the ground ivy weed. For while the horsetail seldom encroaches on American gardens, it will appropriate to itself fallow farmland, railroad embankments, and any meadows or pastureland it can find—especially in the West and in regions of America having a soil rich in clay. Indeed, it was once a curse to American ranchers who claimed that their cattle and sheep suffered ruinous epidemics of diarrhea after eating this ever-present weed.

There are many people who consider the horsetail not merely odd-looking, but grotesque. For with its leafless stems "graced" only by scaly sheaths at their joints, the plant resembles nothing so much as a moth-eaten asparagus. These unlovely stems are multiple-branched, furrowed, and green in color. They are so hard that Colonial housewives of pre-Revolutionary times and the years right after used them to scour out their butter churns and cooking pots. Hence the nickname "scouring rush." And cabinetmakers of the newly born nation found that horsetail stems made excellent sandpaperlike buffers.

Horsetail's upper growths are like surfaced periscopes because they give no indication of the industrious bulk of underground ramifications. They spring from hairy, dark brown, branching stems boring several feet deep into the ground and bearing dark tubers that are ready and very willing to be detached to form new plants.

So strong is this underground network of roots, that farmers and construction workers attempting to dig with a spade or shovel in a field claimed by horsetails will often be stymied in their efforts. Consequently, to get through the root-infested soil, they must call in heavy tractors or bulldozers. And the problem is compounded because often there are no plant growths above the ground to let these puzzled men know what it is they are struggling against.

Besides propagating by detached tubers, the horsetail sows new plants in March and April. In those months, the weed sends forth unbranched *brown* shoots covered with scaly whorls and topped with a conelike crown. These specialized shoots then proceed to scatter their dust-fine spores. (For horsetails, like ferns and many older, now vanished orders, reproduce by means of an alternation of plant generations.)

Troublesome as it is, the horsetail can be put to good use. It has a great capacity to absorb soil nutrients and anything else in the earth which it fancies. This was proved many years ago when a Polish physiologist who had burned a large crop of horsetail unexpectedly recovered a visible amount of gold from its ashes! This unlooked-for hoard was an early indication of the ability of all plants to secrete elements according to their availability and according to the particular plant's individual taste.

This gold-digger can also secrete very useful quantities of cobalt and calcium, and of silica. This last is a particularly potent fungicide for deterring black spot on roses and

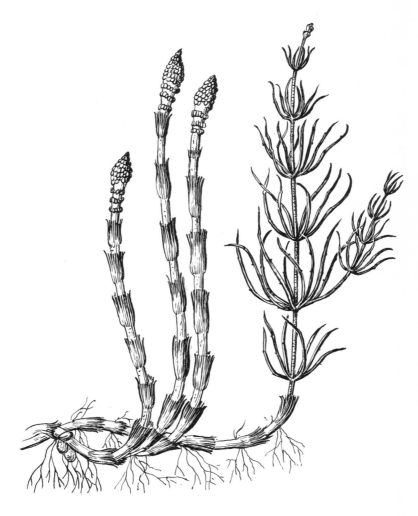

**HORSETAIL: On the left, the spore-bearing shoots;
on the right, the mature (but sterile) plant**

mildew on any plant. So the horsetail can be made to provide an excellent folia spray that not only remedies plant deficiencies, but frustrates fungus attacks as well. Although the horsetail persists in fields and plains, it is comforting to know that it can be made to disgorge its properties for the benefit of more splendid and less furtive plants. In fact, the horsetail is so good for garden plants that the dried weed should be bought to make a plant tonic similar in composition to the commercial "Preparation 508." This is infused from the stems that arise after the unbranched brownish shoots, bearing the spores, have disappeared in late May. These succeeding branching shoots, resembling little pine trees, are the richest in silica and may be used either fresh or dried. To make this spray, cover $1\frac{1}{2}$ ounces of dried horsetail with 5 quarts of cold water and bring it to a boil. Simmer for 20 minutes only, then take it off the stove and leave it to cool, covered, for 24 hours. The next day, strain the liquid free from bits and use it.

If fresh plants are to be used, put two good handfuls in a cooking pan and cover them with water. Simmer for 20 minutes, then allow this compound to cool and infuse, covered, for 24 hours. The next day, strain your solution and dilute it with two parts of water to one of the infusion.

Once a week, spray all your garden foliage with the infusion-tonic until the greenery drips. Then water all the plant roots with horsetail tea (see page 32). The infusions are not in any way harmful or poisonous to plants, even if the horsetail solution is used in unnecessarily strong proportions to the water.

Horsetail tea can also be used as a spray to prevent mint rust and the rust that attacks mallows, such as hollyhocks (prevalent fungus diseases). Moreover, it is an ancient remedy for human ills. Herbalists still respect its soothing and curative effects on disordered bladders and also use it to battle inflammations, reduce swellings, and clear up ugly skin eruptions.

Lamb's-quarters

LAMB'S-QUARTERS is also known as white goosefoot, bacon weed, muckweed, muck-hill weed, midden myles, dung weed, pigweed, and fat hen (an almost exclusively British term for this herb). No one should pay any attention to these vulgar labels, however. It is a venerable weed—and one of considerable importance. Just recently in fact, lamb's-quarters was submitted to laboratory analysis designed to prove—or disprove—its claims to another popular name, "All Good" (a surprisingly complimentary title for a little weed that has had so many vile nicknames hurled at it). These laboratory tests revealed that All Good contains more iron and protein than either raw cabbage or spinach. It has more vitamin B1 than raw cabbage and more vitamin B2 than raw cabbage or spinach. As regards its mineral content: it has more calcium than raw cabbage, and its other constituents compare favorably with our most popular table vegetables.

This common plant persists as a weed, reveling on any farmer's manure pile or country housewife's kitchen-refuse heap. It frolics, too, over pasturelands and will tolerate almost any waste ground in North America, the British Isles, Continental Europe, Africa, Asia, and Australia. Only to South America does it deny the favor of its presence (although another species of goosefoot, the *Chenopodium quinoa* is cultivated in the Andean region for its nutritious seeds). At one time lamb's-quarters was the most valued vegetable in man's diet. And any surplus of the plant was used as cattle fodder. As its recent analysis has shown, these early Europeans made a good choice.

Lambs'-quarters lost favor only after its relative, the upstart, spinach, was introduced from southwest Asia in the sixteenth century. But it left its name in a number of places. It was the "melde" of the Anglo-Saxons (from the Old Norse *meldr*, the Vikings' word for a certain quantity of ground meal—and referring to the texture of the leaves' undersides, as we shall see below). As "melde," it grew so profusely in some areas that the settlements of these early Britons were named after it. For instance, the tenth-century hamlet Meldeburna (meaning "the stream where melde grows") in Cambridgeshire survives today as the town of Melbourn. And there was Meldinges in Suffolk, now Milden. Many other places have names that probably have their roots in this "myles" or "melde" of the Anglo-Saxons. For the plant's abundant haunts were too desirable for early food-seekers to pass them by. They simply had to stop, build their crude shelters, and stay on for at least a few generations.

Fossils show us that this plant was growing in Britain in the late-glacial and the post-glacial periods of that country. It was in the accustomed diet of the Neolithic, Bronze Age, and early Iron Age people. Even the cultivated Romans and other later diners enjoyed this herb regularly.

Lamb's-quarters is a rather unlovely annual growing from 1 to 3 feet tall. It has a spire shape. Its short, alternate-branched stems may be reddish streaked or they may be plain green. The stalked leaves, too, are variable; some are narrow, some are wide-pointed ovals with toothlike indentations, and others are almost triangular with wavy teeth. The many clusters of minute, pale green flowers come in short spikes from the axils of the upper leaves. The leaves and stems, and especially the undersides of the leaves, are powdered with meal (coarse, grainy particles) of a whitish-gray. This meal gives the plant its species name, *album* (meaning "white"). Its full botanical name is *Chenopodium album*, meaning—rather fancifully—"goose" (from the Greek word *chen*) and "little foot" (from the Latin *podium*).

Lamb's-quarters belongs to the *Chenopodiaceae* family, which includes such well-known vegetables as the beet-root, Harvard beet, sugar beet, spinach, and Swiss chard. Moreover, the genus *Chenopodium* contained in this family has many species of goosefoot plants other than the lamb's-quarters. These close relatives of our weed have such names as "stinking goosefoot," "red goosefoot," "upright goosefoot," "nettle-leaved goosefoot," "fig-leaved goose-foot," "wormwood goosefoot," and many similar ones. All the goosefoot plants are so alike that it is difficult to tell which is which.

One "cousin" of our white goosefoot, Good King Henry (*Chenopodium bonus-henricus*) was a favorite vege-table of Merrie Old England. But some years ago this goosefoot, too, went completely out of fashion. Today, however, it has triumphantly returned, imported and expensive now, to be sold in gourmet London shops. Let us hope that the much-maligned lamb's-quarters will soon also find a place among elite vegetables on both sides of the Atlantic.

Meanwhile, it is a weed to be encouraged, even to be grown from seed if it is not already in the garden. For it is nutritious and needs no cultivation. Once established, it

LAMB'S-QUARTERS

109

will sow itself to supply your kitchen with greens when other cresses are scarce. The young seedlings are good in salads, and the tips of the older plants can be taken before they seed to make a tender delicacy. The leaves should be cooked as a vegetable and they will also make a bracing, bright green soup for winter menus.

In times past, the seeds of lamb's-quarters were harvested all over Europe, to be dried and ground into flour for making bread, cakes, and gruel. In parts of America they are still used for that purpose. (I have already mentioned a goosefoot plant, closely related to the lamb's-quarters, which is a valued agricultural crop in the Andes by virtue of its seeds.) Lamb's-quarters seeds resemble buckwheat in flavor and, even when eaten raw, are quite pleasant. They were an ingredient of the gruel eaten by the hanged Tollund chieftain as his last meal (see our discussion on page 9).

Apart from its food value, there is another good reason for growing this weed. It is a friendly herb to other plants. Its deep roots plumb the far recesses of the soil. And in this way the mineral nutrients that lie in solution there are raised to within reach of the lamb's-quarters' shallower-rooted companions. In addition, its leaf-spread catches and carries water to its less-endowed neighbors. It is a plant to be interspersed among the other tenants of your garden. You will not be taking full advantage of lamb's-quarters' excellent effects on other plants if you allow this weed to monopolize a single, concentrated plot of ground.

An old English recipe says "Boil myles in water and chop them in butter and you will have a good dish." But if you use the plant as a vegetable this is too careless an instruction for the tastiest results. It is better to wash the leaves and their small stalks in cold water and then put them dripping wet into a saucepan. Add a spoonful of water (no more) to prevent their burning. Cook them over a low heat and keep moving the leaves. When they are cooked, drain and press out the water. Then chop the leaves finely and return them to the pan to reheat, with a light seasoning of salt and pepper plus a dash of nutmeg and a good chunk of butter or margarine. Stir together and serve hot.

For soup: Wash a good handful of the leaves and their small stalks and put them into a saucepan with $1\frac{1}{4}$ pints of cold water, a little salt, and a tablespoonful of polished rice. (Do not use any "instant," prepared mix.) Cook this mixture with the potlid on until the greenery is tender. Then strain the liquid into an enamel bowl and rub the solids through a sieve to make a purée. Thin this down to the desired consistency with the strained liquid and some milk. Now add a dash of nutmeg and pepper and return your thinned purée to the pan to simmer with a good chunk of butter. Beat it with an old-fashioned egg beater as it simmers, until it is blended. It must not boil. When it is sufficiently heated and blended, remove the pan from the stove and add a little thick cream. (Or you may use the top sediment of unhomogenized milk, if you wish.) And to bind the soup in true French manner, pour it into a tureen containing the yolk of an egg that has been beaten with a little of the cooking liquid.

A different flavor can be achieved by cooking a few shallots that have been previously fried in butter along with your lamb's-quarters leaves. A small onion is also an interesting innovation.

Ox-Eye Daisy

OX-EYE DAISY, known as marguerite, moon daisy, dog daisy, maudlin daisy, or *Chrysanthemum leucanthemum* by the botanists, is a familiar wild plant in all parts of Europe and Russian Asia just as it is in parts of America. (Until 1941, North Carolina claimed the ox-eye as its official state flower.) It is one of the commonest of all wild plants and, with its golden disc surrounded by rays of gleaming white petals crowning a tough, scantily leafed stalk (up to 2 feet tall), it appears as sheets of white wherever it is allowed to flourish.

I have a special affection for this brilliant white daisy, partly for the ages-long folklore attached to it, and because it was my mother's favorite flower. Curiously, she did not know how apt was her choice. She was an ardent suffragette, and this bloom was dedicated by the ancient Greeks to Artemis (Latin, Diana), the moon-goddess guardian of women's interests and succor of certain of their diseases. In Christian times the plant, with that goddess' attributes, was transferred to Saint Mary Magdalene's sphere of influence. The moon daisy was then called "maudelyn" or "maudlin" after her. (This ancient English pronunciation is still used for Magdalen College at Oxford and Magdalene College, Cambridge.) Because Artemis was a daughter of the Thunder God, the goddess' emblem flower was also called "thunder daisy" and credited with the daughter's powers against the Olympian

OX-EYE DAISY

father's lightning strikes. As a result, the plant was kept in gardens to be handy against storms—or women's needs.

As this daisy flowered around midsummer, it was held to be obviously beloved by St. John. Therefore, on and around June 24, the day of his festival, in every country of the northern hemisphere garlands of his flowers were hung upon houses and churches. Then it was called "St. John's Daisy" and "solstice flower." An old name was "Baldur's Brow" for the Norsemen's god of light and peace, from whose brow issued a glory of light.

According to Dioscorides, the noted physician-writer who at one time was also attached to Nero's army, the fresh or dried flowers of the ox-eye daisy were of great service as a curative tea and as a lotion to bathe hard swellings. He also held it to be a cure for jaundice. Indisputably, it was a valuable herb for dressing wounds.

Later herbalists also esteemed the plant. One says that the flowers "cast forth beams of brightness" and he continues: "The whole herb, stalks, leaves, and flowers, boyl'd in posset-drink, and drunk, is accounted an excellent remedy for an asthma, consumption, and difficulty of breathing."

This daisy remains a curative herb employed by herbalists. It has much the same action as camomile. The flowers are balsamic and make an effective infusion—1 ounce to $1\frac{1}{4}$ pints boiling water (see page 33)—for relieving coughs and night sweats and for clearing bronchial catarrh. The tea made from the whole plant has given good results in cases of whooping cough, asthma, and nervous disorders. The root, too, provides a remedy for checking night sweats suffered during pulmonary disorders. Externally, the infusions act as healing lotions for bruises, sores, ulcers, and some skin complaints.

This daisy is obviously of the *Compositae* family, and as happens with other chrysanthemums, all its parts are edible. The leaves supply a pleasant tangy taste in salads, and the tasty white petals make the dish more attractive and beneficial when sprinkled over the greenery.

Potentilla

POTENTILLA is the generic name for more than fifty species of wild plants occurring in America. (Great Britain has only nine species growing wild.) The two potentillas most common as garden weeds in Anglo-American lands are the silverweed and the cinquefoil. Both are lovely wild plants, being of the rose family. In fact, if silverweed were less invasive, it could merit for itself a place on the edge of the most elegant flower bed, by virtue of its exquisite foliage. And quite apart from their beauty, we should have a warm feeling toward these weeds because the potentillas are so closely intermingled with human history.

As their generic name implies, they are potent herbs. Indeed, so powerful are their medicinal qualities that we can document their use all the way back to the time of the first Greek doctors. And they remain in the employment of the most modern herbalists.

"Silverweed," "fern-buttercup," "prince's feathers," "goose grass," "midsummer silver," "silver fern," and the especially apt "traveler's ease" are among the charming common names for the *Potentilla anserina*. The species name means "goose," from the Latin *anser*. This may have been given as a token of appreciation because these birds—esteemed in Rome since the time they reportedly saved the city by waking its sleeping garrison—enjoyed eating the plant's feathery leaves that are silvered and shining with downy white hairs. Or perhaps they simply suggested

SILVERWEED

117

goose feathers to the people who so named them long ago. These decorative leaves could give a fine pattern and contrast in a garden border, just as they enhance floral arrangements indoors, with their long, tapering midrib sprouting pairs of serrated leaflets on either side. The flowers are rather flat and of a pale gold color, but they are too sparse and fleeting to be useful. In design, they resemble strawberry blossoms or, naturally enough, miniature wild roses. And there is a cousin to the silverweed, a third potentilla quite common in the north temperate zones, whose blossoms have such a phenomenal resemblance to strawberries that it is familiarly called the "barren strawberry" plant.

Silverweed is an almost universal plant that spreads from Lapland to New Zealand, from China to Chile, with no qualms about the soil it grows in. Once valued as a friendly herb, it was cultivated as a crop from prehistoric times until fairly recently for its roots. These taste like parsnips and make good eating. They were consumed raw, boiled, or roasted. And often they were dried to be ground into flour for bread and gruel.

The plant has medicinal and cosmetic properties, too. Being full of astringent tannin, it was used to heal ulcers; dissolve gallstones; and beautify spotty, freckled, and sunburned complexions. The leaves, by nature cool, soothed hot, tired feet and were a well-known comfort to foot travelers and those porters and lackeys who trudged the long roads with—or in place of—pack animals. In days of old, footmen, runners, and marching soldiers would rest by the wayside and fill up their footwear with these fresh, relieving leaves.

"Cinquefoil" (meaning five-leafed), "five fingers," "five-leaved grass," and "creeping potentilla" are popular

CINQUEFOIL

names for the attractive *Potentilla reptans*. Indeed, its species name means "creeping." This pleasing garden weed has rich green, long-stalked leaves that in general are composed of five leaflets, although the leaf may produce more when cinquefoil nestles in our richest soil. The long-stemmed, honey-rich, yellow flowers resemble those of silverweed and arise from the leaf axils. They have five petals unless the plant flaunts an extra one or two while enjoying a lush diet.

This was an herb of love potions and of ancient witchcraft. In fact, it was an ingredient in "Witches' Ointment." This was made from "the fat of children digged out of their graves; of the juices of smallage [wild celery], wolfbane [a virulently poisonous species of aconite noted for its medieval ability to repel werewolves], and cinquefoil, mingled with the meal of fine wheat." Paradoxically, it was also credited with supernatural powers that would keep witches and evil spirits at bay. No doubt this attribution came from the spiritual significance of the five spreading leaflets, which may have reminded people of the fingers of their benevolent manor priest outstretched in benediction. But apart from its use in spells and charms, cinquefoil was a medicinal herb with a high reputation for relieving gout, cancer, throat troubles, and many other complaints. And, like countless other familiar remedies of their homelands, it was carefully taken into America by early settlers.

Both silverweed and cinquefoil have similar methods of embarrassing gardeners: Each has a blackish, foot-long taproot that firmly anchors a rosette of leaves. From any leaf axil comes a slender prostrate branch (a dozen or more from each rosette and arranged as spokes of a wheel). It is no unusual achievement for these runners to travel 6 feet from the parent, touching down every 5 or 6 inches to produce rooted tufts of leaves. Next season the chains of little plants are themselves mature parents, each with a long taproot and eager, emigrating runners. Thus, one potentilla can colonize more than 12 square yards in one growing season.

The seeds of these lively weeds can come into any garden in manure. Or they may be brought in by birds, who always find plenty of these particular seeds to feed upon. Indeed, the source of supply is limitless. For besides embellishing the countryside, the potentillas grow quite happily in both city and suburb. If housing developments should encroach upon their open fields or thicket sites, they will just as philosophically make their homes along the new roadsides or in city parks, demolition areas, and the rare patches of waste ground. Excluding their taproots, both weeds are honest enough to make their network on the surface, unlike some weedy rogues with underground traveling habits. If they are in the garden, or are available in nearby fields, it is good to know that the whole plants, root and leaf, have the same enriching, curative virtues. Silverweed and cinquefoil have many beneficial constituents, but they are particularly rich in an easily assimilated calcium. For this mineral alone, they ought to be valued for feeding plants or making a simple domestic medicine. The tea infused from them (1 ounce to $1\frac{1}{4}$ pints of boiling water) provides a good mouthwash and gargle for ulcerated mouths. Or it can be used to relax sore and constricted throats. The tisane also makes an efficient lotion for clearing up pimples and closing open pores. Moreover, it soothes painful sunburn. The ordinary infusion taken as a tea, reinforced by a stronger brew in quantities large enough to be used as a bathing lotion, is recommended for relieving bleeding piles. How true the old apothecaries' claim is of silverweed's ability to fix loose teeth, I don't know.

By this time we can see why the silverweed and cinquefoil should be among our most tolerated weeds. No one will want a garden overrun by these charming encroachers, but certainly whole colonies of them should not be uprooted callously and brusquely. Even if we are no connoisseurs of beauty (and there are few gardeners who fall into that negative category), we cannot ignore these weeds' medicinal value. And the gardener sensitive to history will appreciate these potentillas for the healing services they performed among those ancient peoples whose civilizations inspired our own—and for the psychological comfort they provided medieval man.

Purslane

PURSLANE, green purslane, pigweed, or *Portulaca oleracea* is a member of the small *Portulacaceae* family, which includes some showy flowering plants indigenous to South America and the tropics. But the purslane is a modest bloomer and concentrates on producing edible leaves and stems. This type is distributed almost all over the world as an herbaceous annual. It travels over many parts of Europe and Asia and where it is not a "weed" it is cultivated in herb gardens. As a weed in America, purslane offers its tasty parts free, with no sowing or pampering required. The round succulent stem, about 6 inches high, bears in clusters small, oblong, smooth, dark green stalked leaves that are thick and fleshy so long as the plant does not lack water. These are ready for the salad bowl. The flowers are merely functional and must be removed because they make the plant tough and unfit for eating.

The origin of the name "purslane" is unknown. In some ancient herbals it is called "procelayne" and "purcelaine," while in the North American prairies it is "pussly."

This herb has been cultivated and encouraged at all times and was once valued for its power to foil any magic spells that might be cast upon a person or his cattle. The plant was strewn around a bed as protection from evil spirits visiting the apprehensive sleepers. And it was considered to be a sure cure for "blastings by lightning or planets and burning gunpowder."

Medicinally, purslane was recommended for many ailments. Its principal virtues were for cooling fevers, inflammations, dry coughs, and insomnia. Applied to eyes, the bruised herb reduced inflammation; applied to gouty parts, it "easeth pains thereof."

As a culinary herb, purslane offers a variety of uses and it deserves to be brought into the herb bed and encouraged with adequate watering. The fresh young leaves stripped from the tough stems are good in salads: they are cooling and appetite-provoking. A picturesque salad recipe comes from Giles Rose, a master cook to England's Merry Monarch, Charles II: "Take of the newest Purslan, pick and wash it very well, swing it out and land it round of the plate and Lettice round about it, garnish the brims with chervil and flowers of divers colors, very small." This makes a pretty, historical dish. Just picture the bright green lettuce with purslane's darker leaves and red-gold stems, both trimmed with chervil's or carrot's lace and enlivened by edible blossoms such as borage, anchusa, marigold, rosemary, violet, and rose petals.

Purslane's older shoots are enjoyable when cooked as a potherb in soups and stews. And the thick stems of plants that have run to seed are excellent for pickling in the following way:

Wash and dry the purslane and then put it into an enameled saucepan. Dissolve a little *bay salt*, and twice the amount of common salt, in sufficient *flat* draught beer to cover the herb. Simmer gently, then drain the mixture through a sieve and pack it into jars. Boil for 10 minutes as much white vinegar as will cover the purslane, with two pieces of bruised ginger root and a few peppercorns. Pour this over the herb and seal the jars when cold.

PURSLANE

125

For a delicious soup, here is a recipe dating from the eighteenth century: "Boil the purslane in pea soup with a little onion. When your purslane is boiled enough, soak some crusts in the broth and garnish them with purslane. Pour over the broth and serve it up hot."

FOR A FRENCH SOUP "bonne femme": Shred finely half a cucumber, a small onion, a lettuce, a good handful of purslane, and a handful of true sorrel or wood sorrel. Place these in a saucepan with a good pat of butter, a dash of nutmeg, pepper, and salt. Simmer and stir for about 20 minutes, then stir in a dessertspoonful of flour. Moisten the roux gradually, adding and stirring in 30 ounces of good stock—chicken or veal. Stir over the heat until the soup boils; then let it simmer for 20 minutes. Turn off the heat and allow the soup to cool a little, then stir in 2 beaten egg yolks, 5 ounces of cream, and a small teaspoonful of brown sugar. Reheat and serve.

Soapwort

SOAPWORT, Bouncing Bet, latherwort, and fullers' herb. Such mundane names of this plant's habits and uses do not give any indication of its attractions. "Wild Sweet William" and "hedge pink" better describe its appearance. Being of the *Caryophyllaceae* family, soapwort is closely related to the *Dianthus* tribe, the carnations and pinks. It is a lusty perennial, and as Culpeper says, "The root creepeth underground far and near." This penchant for traveling makes soapwort an invasive weed where it is not wanted. But what a lovely one! In its wild state, soapwort grows about 2 feet tall, but when cultivated it may attain as much as 4 feet. The thick stems are well furnished with narrow lance-shaped leaves that are borne opposite each other in pairs. These pairs are attached at the base in the characteristic *Dianthus* fashion. The pale pink flowers are borne in clusters as are those of the Sweet William. And while soapwort's flowers give but little scent during daylight, at nightfall they exude a delicious aroma that reminds one of the perfume of the nicotine genus.

The Latin name *Saponaria officinalis* from *sapo* (soap) refers to the lather produced by crushing this plant's leaves. This phenomenon is made possible by their high saponin content, saponin being the determining component of soap. Resin, gum, and a mucilage are also present in the leaves. This combination produces an exceptional cleansing quality, and for this reason, soapwort has been widely used for many centuries by textile manufacturers in need of a special substance for washing their wools, linens, and silks. It is still cultivated for this purpose in Syria, Arabia, and other Eastern countries.

The plant acquired its species name, *officinalis* (translated "of the shops"), because it was always available in herb shops. For soapwort was in demand for ordinary cleaning long before fancy soaps were invented. It was also valued as an antiseptic for cleansing wounds and sores.

Medicinally, soapwort has been employed for treating kidney and bladder upsets and has been particularly effective in curing skin diseases. The Tudor herbalist, Gerard, tells us that he used soapwort "with happy success in the most contumacious diseases, but it is of somewhat an ungrateful taste and therefore it must be reserved for the poorer sort"! Modern herbalists maintain the plant's curative powers and recommend it for the treatment of jaundice, scrofula, and general skin disorders. Moreover, it has long been credited as a valuable cure for venereal complaints.

As a domestic remedy for skin troubles, a decoction should be made of 2 ounces of soapwort in $1\frac{1}{4}$ pints water. This is to be taken in 1-tablespoonful doses, three times a day.

An interesting and valuable use of soapwort, which has further endeared it to textile manufacturers, lies in its beneficial action on the proteins of silk and wool. So soapwort is also utilized to restore color and sheen to old and faded fabrics, even ancient tapestries, embroideries, and brocades. Its saponin efficiently and harmlessly returns the original luster to delicate china and precious glass. Today it is being used in museums and historic houses to

SOAPWORT

restore their treasures that have been spoiled by ages of neglect.

For Cleaning Fabrics

Tie quantities of the herb in cheesecloth or muslin bags and boil in soft water until foam appears and the water turns greenish. Then soak the material to be washed in cold soft water and continually change it until it is clear. This indicates that the solution has extracted as much of the loose dirt as it can, without a little human "elbow grease."

Then lay the fabric on a board placed over the bathtub if it is a large piece, and apply a sponge in a circular motion. Work the soapy froth gently over the surface. Continue this circular rubbing, with fresh saponaria foam being constantly applied, until there is no longer any dirt left in the material. When it is quite clean, wipe the foam away and dab it off with towels. Then dry the fabric in a cool, airy, *shaded* place.

If embroidery or a tapestry on canvas is to be treated, it should be prepared *before washing* so that immediately after washing it can be fixed on a stretcher to restore its original shape. To do this, you need merely to sew strips of material all around the piece to square the shape, and have a stretcher of four pieces of strong wood ready to use. Then, right after washing, drive thumbtacks through these bits of extra material on the edges of the newly washed fabric onto the stretcher. The wood supports will hold your embroidery or tapestry taut as it dries. And in this way the wet chair seat, cushion, or tapestry panel is pulled gently back into shape and secured.

Soapwort is native to central and southeast Europe and it now grows wild over much of that continent. In most cases, it is an escapee from cultivated areas. For there were many such plots of carefully tended ground in the days when fullers (employees of textile mills whose function it was to scour, press, and otherwise prepare cloth for the seamstresses) depended wholly on this herb for a soaping agent. And of course it was also grown in gardens for domestic use. Because of its usefulness it was taken across the sea to New England by settlers from Wales and from the western counties of Britain, especially Devon and Cornwall. And with it, they took its local British name, "Bouncing Bet." Bet has bounced well in America, as it usually does over damp ground, and there it found a new use for itself. For it turned out that soapwort provides a welcome application to the horrid rash caused by America's villainous poison ivy!

Stinging Nettle

THE STINGING NETTLE is sometimes called the true nettle to distinguish it from the dead-nettle plants, even though the only thing the two types of "nettles" have in common is the appearance of their leaves. (See pages 75–81 for detailed discussion.)

The botanical name of the stinging nettle is, fittingly, *Urtica dioica*. This weed is interesting if only because its encrusted tails of pale green, male or female flowers usually grow on different plants. This somewhat prudish separation of the sexes accounts for the plant's species name. For *dioica* means "two dwellings." Nevertheless, the stinging nettles have an enchanting early-morning festival when the males gaily puff their pale golden pollen into the air to be caught by the females. And the plant-fancier enthralled by novel plant habits will not be disappointed if he drags himself out of bed early enough to catch this graceful ritual.

The weed's generic name, *Urtica* (meaning "to burn and sting") is as old as Pliny, the illustrious Roman who knew both the plant's bite and its great worth. This nettle's flowers are minute and inconspicuous, but they are the only food of the caterpillars of the lovely peacock butterfly and the equally exquisite tortoiseshell butterfly. Therefore we call these bewitching creatures its "flying blossoms" and we must be grateful to the stinging nettle for our enjoyment of them.

Nicholas Culpeper, too, was a great admirer of this

weed even though he did write: "Nettles are so well known, that they need no description; they may be found by feeling for them in the darkest night." For this hint at the pain they inflict merely introduces his long praise of the weed's curative virtues. These were, of course, confined to healing the ailments of man because it was a long time before we gardeners realized that plants can work for the welfare of one another. Yet in this context, nettles are the most valuable of weeds. While growing, they stimulate the growth of other plants nearby and make them more resistant to disease, in the same manner as the foxglove. And nettles, too, improve the storing capacities of root vegetables and of tomatoes.

I recently had an amazing experience of the effect of nettles on bush fruits. I have six old black-currant bushes whose miserable fruits were too small to use. I planted new ones in another place and left the ancient ones uncared for until they were completely hidden by nettles. One day I looked into the green domes and found the poor old bushes loaded with large, juicy fruits. No doubt a good nitrogenous feed, such as composted nettles or dried blood, would have given the invalids a fillip, but I should have missed a very interesting experience.

It is not possible to foster beds of nettles all over the garden, but these weeds should be understood. Moreover, once their values are appreciated, town gardeners may agree that it would be better to return from a trip into the country with a bag of nettles than with bunches of wild flowers. The cut stems and leaves rot down into perfect humus. And when laid on the soil under a covering mulch of manure or straw, they, like the couch grass, do an amazing job of smothering weeds.

Stinging Nettle 133

Stinging nettles thrive on rubbish heaps where the nitrogen bacteria are busy working at their task of breaking up and decaying vegetable matter. In this process they are a symbiotic partnership, the nettle encouraging the bacteria while it simultaneously accumulates large quantities of nitrogen, silica, iron, and mineral salts. It is so active a decomposer and humus-maker that decomposed nettles are used as the catalyst to ferment compost heaps by commercial houses that sell purely organic fertilizers rather than the synthetic, chemical-saturated ones that are so rapidly losing repute. But even the simplest of compost heaps—perhaps the one you are building in the backyard—should have its generous supply of stinging nettles. The finest rich, black humus is to be found in a nettlebed where the stems and leaves have rotted for several seasons. This is the stuff to activate your compost heap, and also to mix with peat when you use this carbonized moss as a mulch. For nettle humus quickens life into the otherwise sterile peat.

A complete plant-food liquid can be made by soaking a sheaf of nettles in a vessel of rainwater for two or three weeks. At the end of that time, the water will contain all the plant's virtues. A liquid fertilizer made from nettles, either fresh or dried, by the usual method (see page 32) is not only a good folia feed, but also an effective spray against mildew, black fly, aphis, and plant lice—both in the greenhouse and outside it.

The nettle's good points are often obscured by its bitter ones. For the stems of this weed are covered with stinging hairs that, once they penetrate the skin, pour acrid formic acid into the man or beast unfortunate enough to encounter this plant's defenses. The pierced area becomes

STINGING NETTLE

swollen and inflamed, and the victim will feel as much pain as if he had been stung by a bee or hornet. There is a way to avoid this distress, however: when it becomes necessary to handle these nettle stems in the garden, grasp the hairs in such a way that they are pressed back into the stem. Then the plant will not be able to sting you.

Although the stinging nettle is common from Maine to Minnesota, and as far south as Missouri, Americans seldom eat them. In Europe, however, they have been used for food and drink for centuries. So valued were they as a potherb and vegetable—and for the tingling flavor they add to homemade teas, wines, and beers—that they were at one time cultivated (along with the dandelion) in most European gardens. In *Rob Roy,* Sir Walter Scott describes an old gardener going about the everyday business of tending his nettles. And the tender young tops of the weed (boiled after picking) still form a staple green in the diet of the country people of Scotland.

It is too bad that American gardeners fail to follow this European example of including young nettle shoots and leaves in their day-to-day cuisine. For this weed is among the most health-giving of all herbs. It is rich, not only in minerals (as a source of iron, it exceeds spinach), but also in vitamin C, recommended by Dr. Linus Pauling to ward off the common cold. A word of warning, nevertheless: Only *young* nettle shoots should be gathered. For in late summer the older ones develop gritty, harmful crystals. And because of the formic-acid content of the weed (the painful agent in its sting), the plant *should not* be eaten raw. Cook the leaves and shoots carefully, as heat dispels any detrimental effects formic acid may have.

Take care, too, that the cooking fumes do not get in

your eyes. All my life I have made stinging nettles an essential part of my own diet and I have never experienced any discomfort while cooking them. However, some people report severe skin and eye irritations after steam laden with the nettle's antiseptic acid has come into contact with their eyes or skin.

I hope you will not be dismayed by these routine warnings. Remember that many generations of European cooks have successfully prepared this green. And in these days of our artificially "enriched" overprocessed foods, the stinging nettle will remedy many of the dietary deficiencies of your family while it provides tasty dishes that they will relish. Following are a few ways to make the stinging nettle so appetizing that it is well worth the effort of a few kitchen precautions.

CREAMED NETTLES: Wear gloves to gather a quantity of young nettle tops. Wash them and shake off the excess water. Now strip off the leaves and put them into a pot with a large lump of butter or margarine. Place the pot over a low flame and cook. From time to time lift the nettle leaves up from the bottom (with a long fork) so that all will be buttered and equally stewed. As the juices begin to flow, add a light seasoning of salt and pepper. When the leaves are thoroughly cooked and tender, strain them well and save the juices to make a delicious soup (see below). Reheat the leaves, stirring in a little more butter and some cream (or the top layer of unhomogenized milk). This vegetable is also very good when cooked with a few chopped chives, shallots, or spring onions.

NETTLE SOUP: The prime ingredient here is the juice saved from the vegetable dish described above. But start by preparing the béchamel sauce that must be combined with your nettle juice. To make this rich cream sauce (named after a gourmet steward of France's Louis XIV), mix a tablespoonful of butter with a tablespoonful of white flour. Stir this mixture over a low flame until it thickens solid. Now add 10 ounces of milk plus salt and pepper to taste, and mix the entire blend well. Now you are ready to pour in the nettle juice! Whip your béchamel sauce continually while you are adding in the nettle juice. If you prefer a richer soup than this, incorporate some grated Cheddar cheese.

NETTLE PORRIDGE OR NETTLE PUDDING:

This tasty treat (sometimes called "porridge" and other times classified as a pudding) is a welcome adjunct to any hot dinner. I enjoy nettles every way the imaginative cook can prepare them. And Samuel Pepys, that man about town in the days when the Stuart kings had just been returned to the throne of Britain, was extremely fond of nettle "porridge." In fact, on February 25, 1661, he made a special note of it in his famous diary: "To Mr Symon's, where we found him abroad, but she, like a good lady, within, and there we did eat some nettle porridge, which was made on purpose to-day for some of their coming, and was very good."

There are many recipes for this savory dish, which is still widely enjoyed in Scotland and the northern counties of England. Several tell us to wrap the mixture in a cloth and then boil the little parcel in salted water. This method causes us to lose a lot of valuable juices, however. The pudding is much better and infinitely more nourishing when the ingredients are steamed in a covered enamel basin. (If a cooking basin is not part of your kitchen equipment, then a shallow, enamel saucepan with sloping sides is the second-best choice. Make very sure that your pan is tightly sealed. For if steam should happen to penetrate the mixture, your pudding will be ruined.)

The Preparation: You will need the following ingredients—

Young nettle leaves: 6 handfuls	Mint: 1 sprig
Young dandelion leaves: 1 handful	Thyme: 1 spray
Watercress: 1 small bunch	Onion: 1
Wood-sorrel leaves: 1 small bunch	Barley: 1 teacupful
Black-currant leaves: 8	

First boil the barley until it is soft. Now wash all your other ingredients and chop them until they are fine. Toss everything into the pot containing your soft barley and mix thoroughly. Season lightly with salt and pepper and add a tablespoonful of butter. Mix again, this time adding a well-beaten egg. Now put your medley into an enamel saucepan, cover it, and let it steam for 90 minutes. Serve the pudding (or porridge) hot with a rich gravy of your choice.

NETTLE WINE: Stinging nettles can also be enjoyed in a pleasant wine consisting of the following ingredients—

Young nettle tops: $2\frac{1}{2}$ quarts	Water: 5 quarts
Sugar: 4 pounds of the best, granulated	Lemons: 2
Ginger root: $\frac{1}{2}$ ounce	Yeast: 1 ounce

First place the 4 pounds of sugar in your fermenting vessel. Now wash the nettletops and shake them in a cloth. Place the washed nettles in the 5 quarts of water and simmer them with the ginger root and thin yellow lemon peel (no white pith) for 45 minutes. As the water evaporates, add more to make up the original 5 quarts. Strain out the solids and add the liquid to the sugar in your fermenting vessel. Stir this new mixture until the sugar is dissolved. When it is cool to lukewarm, add the yeast. Cover tightly with a folded cotton cloth and leave the brew to ferment for 14 days. Then proceed with Stage 2 (page 36).

NETTLE BEER: Unlike the wine, which needs to mature for about a year, the traditional convivial nettle beer can be enjoyed within two weeks of its brewing. It used to be a popular refreshment of country workers. There are numerous recipes for the beer, but the following one is simple and delicious. This lively brew must be contained in glass bottles with strong twist-on caps.

Young cut nettles: 2 pounds   Water: 5 quarts
Lemons: 2   Sugar: 1 pound, Demerara
Cream of tartar: 1 ounce   Yeast: 1 ounce

Place your sugar, cream of tartar, lemon juice, and the thin yellow peel (no white pith) of the lemons in the fermenting vessel. Now rinse the 2 pounds of nettles and shake them in a cloth before boiling them in the water for 15 minutes. Strain the liquor into the fermenting vessel so that it pours onto the ingredients already there. Stir very well, and when the liquor is lukewarm, add the yeast. Place this brew in a warm room and keep it there, covered with a thick folded cloth, for three days. Then strain out all the sediment and bottle the liquid. The beer will be ready to drink in eight days.

The stinging nettle, incidentally, belongs to a very small family, the *Urticaceae*. This family contains only 41 genera, most of which have painful stings, like that of our weed.

Tansy

TANSY, bachelor's button, ginger plant, parsley fern, scented fern—these, along with many other popular names, have been given to this handsome plant that is properly called *Tanacetum vulgare*. Long ago this was one of the most important herbs and a highly decorative plant in every garden. With its rich, dark green, fernlike foliage, it was known in England as "Prince-of-Wales feathers" for the resemblance its leaves bore to the ostrich plumes worn in the prince's helmet and, later, in court headdresses. The leaves being pleasantly aromatic, smelling spicily of ginger, it was called "Stinking Willie." However, in those long ago times, "stink" was the only word in the Anglo-Saxon language expressive of any smell, good or nasty, and it was applied to many delightfully scented plants.

When a compact growth can be achieved—and often this can be induced by planting the herb in a buried bottomless tank or stout cellophane bag and replanting the bag-bound roots every three years—the plant can be a very attractive foliage feature. Indeed, it will become a dense bush, perhaps as tall as 4 feet, bearing loose clusters of tight, yellow, daisylike blooms that look like buttons. The tansy is of the daisy tribe, the *Compositae* family.

The English name "tansy" and the French *tanaisie* are corruptions of *athanasia*, derived from the ancient Greek word for immortality. And it is assumed that Lucian, a famous satirist who lived in the times of Imperial Rome, was referring to this herb in his *Dialogues of the Gods* when he wrote Jupiter's command to Hercules to take away the beautiful youth Ganymede, whom the king of the gods had stolen from earth: "And when he has tasted immortality let him return to us, and he shall be our cupbearer." Another plausible reason for the name is the plant's use, in former eras, to preserve corpses. And for the same virtue, it was rubbed over meat in summer to preserve it from blowflies.

Tansy's ability to repel insects made it a popular medieval strewing herb, as it was particularly effective in coping with the flies and fleas that bred abundantly on floors. In those days when even manor floors remained many inches thick with stale strewings and the debris from uncouth diners and their equally unrestricted animals, proliferating insect pests were a major discomfort of life.

But the main reason why tansy was held in such great esteem was its medicinal qualities. It was considered one of the best springtime remedies to combat the ravages of winter's restricted diet of salted fish and meat. The herb was eaten and tansy tea was drunk until the seventeenth century. Then, at that time the Church claimed tansy as a holy herb commemorative of the Bitter Herbs of the Passover and ruled that it was to be consumed only at Easter. This dictate so annoyed Nicholas Culpeper that in 1652 he wrote "Now, forsooth, tansies must be eaten only on Palm and Easter Sundays and their neighbour days" and he stressed that the "want of commonly eating this herb in spring makes people sickly in summer."

A well-known use for the herb was to induce pregnancy, and to quote Culpeper again: "Let those women that

TANSY

desire children love this herb; 'tis their best companion, their husbands excepted." For this achievement he recommended it either bruised and laid on the navel or boiled in beer and drunk to avoid miscarriages.

Tansy's other services were to dispel worms in children (for which it is still widely used in herbal preparations). A cupful of the tea ought to be drunk night and morning while the subject is fasting. To relieve hysteria or nausea, and to correct weakness of the kidneys, a wineglassful of the tea should be taken in frequent doses. The infusion is 1 ounce of tansy to $1\frac{1}{4}$ pints of boiling water (see page 33). And poultices of tansy leaves have long been valued for relieving the pains of rheumatism and gout.

Besides being cultivated as a medicinal plant, tansy was once also grown for its culinary uses. It is bitter in bulk, but a small quantity goes a long way to enhance a salad— and as a flavoring for tansy pancakes and tansy pudding.

TANSY PANCAKES: Beat 2 eggs, add 5 ounces cream, 2 tablespoonfuls of flour, and 1 ounce of sugar. Beat together very well and then add a teaspoonful of tansy juice with a dash of nutmeg. Beat again and fry as pancakes in a pan greased with butter. Serve hot, garnished with sections of orange and dredged with sugar.

TANSY PUDDING: Boil 3 ounces of ground rice in $1\frac{1}{4}$ pints of milk until it is soft. Then add $\frac{1}{4}$ pound of butter and 3 well-beaten eggs plus sugar and rose water to taste. Beat some tansy leaves in a stoneware pot and squeeze the juice through cheesecloth. Now blend it well into the mixture. Pour into a buttered dish and bake gently for about 45 minutes. When you serve it, top the entire pudding with half sections of orange.

This plant had enjoyed so good a reputation in Europe that according to John Josselyn's *New England Rarities,* published in 1672, the settlers had already introduced it into the New World by that year. It was so well suited to America that it romped away over the Eastern States as a wilding and became a familiar, invasive weed! When planted in gardens, tansy must be lovingly disciplined to be enjoyed.

Toadflax

TOADFLAX. Yellow toadflax, common toadflax, yellow rod, and snapdragon are but a few of the popular names applied to this pretty, naughty weed. It so resembles the garden *Antirrhinum* that it is often mistaken for the wild form of cultivated *Antirrhinum*. As such it has been taken into gardens by myriads of innocent, kindly, and appreciative plant lovers who are then faced with the problem of eradicating the persistent, creeping, avaricious roots: a charming villain in a rock garden!

Toadflax is properly called *Linaria vulgaris* because its foliage resembles that of *Linum,* flax. It is of the same family as the *Antirrhinum*, the *Scrophulariaceae* which includes numerous very varied plants. (Indeed, the foxglove, great mullein, and some other plants of exceptional medicinal worth belong to the *Scrophulariaceae* family.)

This garden intruder sends up erect stems clothed with long narrow leaves that are smooth and hairless and of a bluish-green. The stems terminate in compact masses of pale yellow flowers having orange, swollen underlips. This is the gay invitation for long-tongued bees to alight and force open the tightly closed mouth in order to reach the honey in the long yellow spur. This cunning device also excludes beetles and other unproductive marauders from entering the colorful interior. When the bee emerges from the flower, it is powdered with pollen and ready to fertilize the next bloom it visits.

TOADFLAX

This common toadflax is at home blooming on dry banks and waysides all over Europe—except Portugal. It is also especially fond of making its home among the rows of shrubs and trees which customarily define the borders of European tilled fields. In America, it probably made its debut as seeds in grain sacks. However, it may have been deliberately taken to the New World by settlers who were familiar with its medicinal value. Once introduced, it flourished; became naturalized; and romped over any available sandy, gravelly soil, becoming an especially abundant weed in chalky or limestone districts. It provides juices that are a rich diet for the larvae of certain species of moths and a welcome headquarters for various beetles.

This plant possesses an acrid oil containing several beneficial constituents and it has been used in medicine from very ancient times. The oil is astringent and especially cleansing for the liver. It is not surprising, then, that toadflax is recommended by herbalists for ordinary cases of liver upsets or jaundice. Skin infections and the wretched disease scrofula can also be treated with it.

A green ointment made from the fresh plant has a high reputation for curing piles, sores, ulcers, and skin eruptions. This is easily made by boiling the chopped fresh herb in fine lard until it is crisp and then straining. A poultice made of the fresh weed gives relief from hemorrhoids.

The tea is an infusion of 1 ounce of toadflax to $1\frac{1}{4}$ pints boiling water (see page 33) and may be taken in wineglassful doses several times a day. As a lotion, this same infusion is excellent for bathing inflamed eyes or skin eruptions.

According to old Scandinavian lore, toadflax works in yet another way to benefit the health of gardeners. It has long been the custom in those northern reaches of the world to make an effective fly poison from toadflax. When boiled in milk and set about the house, this brew will attract flies to their doom—and wreak no harmful effects on the other inmates of the homestead.

The old idea that toadflax is poisonous to humans is quite without foundation.

Wild Carrot

WILD CARROT, Queen Anne's Lace, pig's parsley, bird's nest, or *Daucus carota* probably originated on the seacoasts of southern Europe and from there spread throughout that continent and later into Russian Asia and parts of India. And by the same route it has become prolific in America. Although this wilding prefers to grow near the sea, it is often found happily established on wastelands, field borders, and roadsides. From there it is but a simple step into the fertile garden where, as a weed, it can be enjoyed in many different ways. The use of its feathery leaves for floral arrangements is merely the most obvious one.

The whole plant has curative virtues that have been exploited from the most ancient of times—and they are *more* powerful than those of the cultivated carrot. The herb provides an effective tisane that will relieve certain complaints such as the bladder disorders that cause urine retention. Kidney troubles and dropsies (excessive accumulation of body fluids) also respond to carrot tea. When taken night and morning, this is also a useful defense against the gravel and stone formed by the lithic acid of a gouty disposition. The tisane is made by infusing 1 ounce of the herb in $1\frac{1}{4}$ pints boiling water (see page and is taken in wineglassful doses. Half a teaspoonful of bruised seeds is an excellent cure for flatulence, wii colic, chronic coughs, and dysentery. The seeds were o considered a cure for jaundice and were prescribed at

WILD CARROT

onset of dropsies. They have a pleasant aromatic smell and a pungent taste.

All parts of the wild carrot plant have strong antiseptic qualities that prevent putrid changes in the body. The roots were once employed to make pain-killing poultices for cancerous ulcers. The leaves were coated with honey and then applied as cleansing dressings to running sores and ulcers.

The carrot contains a good supply of vitamin A for promoting growth and healthy eyes and skin. It also contains a fair amount of vitamin E. This is important because our intake is rapidly decreasing as a result of the processing and refining of modern foodstuffs. These two vitamins, working together, protect the lungs against the present-day hazards of air pollution. However, the yield of these precious elements is negligible from the raw carrot. Only when it is cooked can we take full advantage of its vitamin contribution.

Wild carrot's culinary gifts are fresh young leaves for salads, and like the seeds, they enrich the flavor of soups and stews. The seeds can also be used in place of caraway seeds when you are boiling cabbage or making cakes.

It is probable that the fleshy, succulent-rooted, cultivated carrot evolved from a southern European variety, the *Daucus carota (var.) sativa.* At any rate it is certain that the thin woody root of the wild type had been fattened up to provide the ancient Greeks with this highly esteemed vegetable. For such it is held to be in several of their writings. In Roman times, Dioscorides' description of the carrot then in use exactly fits the modern kind. Pliny, too, says it is "grown either from the root transplanted or else from seed, the ground being dug to a very considerable depth for the purpose." He tells us that the finest carrots of his day came from Crete.

From classical times to the present, the carrot has been cultivated in Europe. In Britain, it was merely imported until, during the terrible religious persecutions on the continent, Flemish refugees fleeing into England introduced it as a commercially cultivated crop. This occurred during the reign of Queen Elizabeth I. In fact, for the festivities of one of this lady's cunning courtship maneuvers, the royal pavilion was decorated with sprays of flowers and carrots.

"Queen Anne's Lace," the wild plant was called because its finely cut, lacy leaves were so often inserted in the fashionable headdresses and bouquets of the seventeenth, eighteenth, and nineteenth centuries. And its popular use in this way was first—and forever—associated with that monarch's elegant reign. For these stylish elaborations the thick ends of the carrots were cut off and set in a saucer of water until they sprouted a usable tuft of greenery. If the remaining stems were then wrapped in damp moss, the supply could be kept going. (This is still a good method of enjoying their fern foliage in winter flower arrangements.)

The carrot belongs to the large family *Umbelliferae,* whose plants bear their tiny blossoms in flat, umbrellalike clusters. When the carrot seeds ripen, the umbels contract into a curious hollow cup shape that gives the plant its descriptive name "bird's nest."

When you feel energetic enough or sufficiently provoked to dig up wild-carrot roots, here is a recipe for a potent country brew. If you lack wild ones, cultivated carrots may be used.

Carrot whisky

6 pounds carrots	1 ounce chopped raisins
2 oranges	1 pound clean wheat
2 lemons	1 ounce yeast
4 pounds sugar	5 quarts water

Wash the roots well and boil them in the water until tender. Strain off the liquid and add to it the sugar, raisins, and wheat plus the thin yellow peel (no white pith) of the fruits and the juice. Stir this mixture until the sugar is dissolved. Now heat only a cupful of this liquid until it is lukewarm and sprinkle the yeast into it. When the cupful froths, add it to the "wine." Leave the vessel covered with a clean cloth for about two weeks, stirring daily. Then proceed with Stage 2 (detailed on page 36).

Wild Roses

IT MAY SEEM STRANGE to include a rose species in a book devoted to weeds—except to the reader who has suffered from their invasion. Once introduced, certain types become so invasive that they are difficult to control. *Rosa rugosa* is one example that qualifies as a weed. This lusty plant, which originated in Japan, northern China and parts of Korea, has spread into Europe and America by all the means at its disposal. And it was further encouraged by rose-fanciers. Thus, undaunted in the West for only a century, it has become so firmly naturalized that it is now regarded as a wild rose in many parts of the New World as well as the Old.

Rugosa is a beautiful rose with rugose (meaning wrinkled), dark green leaves that are softly hairy on the undersides. The large, single, fragrant flowers are of a delightful bright purplish-pink—a magenta to which I am addicted. This species is also aptly named the "hedgehog rose" as the stems are extremely well-protected by an armory of closely set, tough prickles. And in the Orient, this wild rose is known in yet a third way: as the "Ramanas rose." This label, probably derived from the Japanese word *ramman,* which means "blooming profusely," is also appropriate. For the roots of the *rugosa* continually explore the ground and send up a remarkable profusion of new growths.

Indeed, a *rugosa* introduced into a garden for the

pleasure of its flowers and fruits (which are among the most decorative of all rose hips) will take over in so determined a manner that the gardener, unable to cope, is usually driven to shift all other plants from its vicinity and allow it to form its desired family circle. My own specimen comes up between the closely set flagstones of the terrace as it crosses over into the flower beds beyond. For me, this is an annoying weed when it springs up away from the original splendid bush.

As a result of its strong growth, *rugosa* has been extensively used as the most robust stock available for grafting other roses. In many instances when these grafts have failed, the stock has succeeded and flourished, so that it lives on in old gardens, or where old gardens have disappeared. It has formed thickets in hedgerows—those charming rows of shrubs and trees which English and European farmers so often plant to establish the boundaries of their lawns and fields. Similarly, it blooms enchantingly along roadsides and country lanes. Today its sale is being mightily encouraged as a hedge plant that will effectively defend gardens from intruders. But perhaps its greatest claim to our appreciation is that it has been the parent stock for some hybrids of more than ordinary vigor and hardiness. Notable among these treasures are the whitest of white roses, the *Blanc double de Coubert;* the lovely silvery-pink-flowered Conrad F. Meyer rose; and the delightfully different F. J. Grootendorst rose with its clusters of small fringed flowers.

Like any other rose, *rugosa* should be used as much as possible for its health-giving properties. Leaf, petal, and hip (the fruit of the rose plant, formed after the blossom itself dies and identified by a bulging of the stem just

WILD ROSE

under the wilted flower) all have their uses. Dried rose leaves make a pleasantly fragrant and beneficial tea. Brewed to be drunk like ordinary tea, it is soothing and astringent. Indeed, it cools the blood, acts kindly on the liver and stomach, and can cure a tickling cough. Fresh leaves go well into salads. And the gay pink petals are an attractive embellishment for both desserts and salads. Candied rose petals make delightful decorations for a number of sweet dishes and as edible posies on iced cakes. The following recipes for candying rose petals apply just as well to all other edible flowers. And the imaginative cook who chooses to make confections of another type of blossom will find that the inclusion of a few tender rose leaves and mint leaves, properly treated, will further adorn her display.

Rose-Petal Treats

CANDIED PETALS: Gather the petals in dry weather after the dew has evaporated. Clean them in preparation for dipping into royal icing that is thin enough to drain off easily. Make this icing with egg white that is whipped into a stiff froth; add sufficient icing sugar to mix; and then incorporate rose coloring and rose water to your desired flavor. Dip each petal into the icing and place it on a wire tray. Before the icing sets, sprinkle the dipped petals with powdered or granulated sugar, then let them dry in a *very cool* oven with the door open.

CRYSTALLIZED PETALS: This is a traditional recipe. Gather the petals as you would for candying. Have on hand 2 ounces of gum arabic already dissolved in 10 ounces of water. Separate the petals and spread them on a dish.

Spray them with the gum solution and then lift them onto sheets of white paper. Now sprinkle with sugar and leave them to dry for 24 hours. Make a syrup of 1 pound of sugar to 10 ounces of water. Stir until the sugar is dissolved, then boil until the syrup forms a thread in cold water. Color with carmine or cochineal. Now you are ready for the final coating: Put the petals in a shallow dish and pour the syrup over them. Let them soak for another 24 hours, then spread them out on a wire tray and dry them in a cool oven with the door ajar.

CONSERVE (of roses): Old-fashioned delicacies were made with any edible scented flowers. The petals were pounded to pulp with a pestle in a mortar and the mash was then weighed. To every ounce of pulp, the lady of the house allowed 3 ounces of sugar. The mixture was then beaten together very thoroughly before it was placed in containers and sealed. The modern woman will want to use a stoneware pot for the grinding process. And in place of her great-grandmother's pestle she can substitute any heavy, round-end kitchen utensil.

Rose-Hip Products

Rose hips are a very valuable source of vitamin C. Indeed, during World War II they were a prime source of this essential element. Starving populations deprived of their usual nutritious foods were at least able to avoid vitamin C deficiencies by eating their local, uncurtailed rose fruits. For our own purposes, it is well to note that rose hips can be preserved in several pleasant ways (see the recipes on the next pages). And therefore we can enjoy them at all times of the year.

When you are gathering the hips it is advisable to wear gloves as rose hips are so astringent that they can make the fingers insensitive to touch for several days. (This is my own experience.)

ROSE-HIP SYRUP: This should be taken in daily doses of a dessertspoonful. Clean 1 pound of hips and put them through an electric blender. Now transfer them immediately to a saucepan that already holds 25 ounces of boiling water. Boil further, until the mixture seems thoroughly fused, then remove it from the heat and let it stand for 30 minutes. Pour through a hot, thick cloth and allow it to drip. Now put the pulp back into the saucepan with 20 ounces of hot water this time, and boil for a while. Again allow it to stand. Now drain it through a hot, thick cloth as before. Mix the two extractions into an enameled or aluminum saucepan and simmer until the liquid is reduced by half. Then, to make sure no irritating hairs remain, strain again and add $\frac{1}{2}$ pound of sugar. Boil this new mixture for 5 minutes, then pour it at once into dry sterilized bottles. Fill the bottles to about $1\frac{1}{2}$ inches below the corks. Wire or tie down the corks (which must be sterilized by boiling before you use them). Stand the sealed bottles in a large, deep pan that rests on a folded cloth or newspaper. Fill the pan with enough water to reach the base of the corks and keep the water at simmering point for 20 minutes. Remove the bottles and stand them on a wooden surface or a folded newspaper to cool. Finally, dip the corked tops in melted candle wax. Remember that syrups should not be kept for more than a year.

ROSE-HIP JAM: Use ripe, plump, red hips. Wash and

dry them, then cut them open with a sharp, pointed knife and *remove all the seeds and the hairs*. Put them into a preserving pan with enough water to float them. Cook slowly until they are tender. Then rub them through a sieve, weigh the pulp, and allow $\frac{3}{4}$ pound of sugar to each 1 pound of pulp. Boil this compound until the jam sets when tested.

ROSE-HIP WINE: You will need the following ingredients—
Rose hips: 5 pints gathered *after the first frost*
Water: 5 quarts
Sugar: 3 pounds of the best granulated
Yeast: 1 ounce

Wash and drain the hips, then crush them with a mallet or stamp them between clean paper (or cloth) with a flatiron or hammer. Place the crushed hips in the fermentation vessel. Put the sugar and water into a large saucepan and heat, stirring until the sugar is dissolved. Then let this liquid cool and, when it is lukewarm, pour it over the hips. Cream the yeast in a little of the warm liquid, then add it to your brew. Cover the mixture and let it stand until fermentation ceases. Strain through several thicknesses of fine organdie and proceed with Stage 2 (given on page 36).

Wood Sorrel

WOOD SORREL, wood sour, trefoil, hallelujah, three-leaved grass, or shamrock, is known to botanists as *Oxalis acetosella*. It is a member of a very small family, *Oxalidaceae*, with many representatives preferring the tropics. But the delicate little wood sorrel revels in damp shady places almost all over Europe and in parts of America. It is not in any way related to the true sorrels, but it so called for its generous content of the special salt, binoxalate of potash, which is also a constituent of the true sorrels and of rhubarb.

This small plant flourishes in woods and spreads from its perennial rootstock which is covered with bright red scales. From this, all the leaves arise on long slender stalks that are often red-tinted at the base. Each leaf is composed of three heart-shaped leaflets of a delicate yellowish-green on the upper surface and, in general, a rich purple beneath. The leaves are peculiarly sensitive to the plant's need for conserving moisture, and they fold into a neat pyramid when sunshine that would cause evaporation lights upon them. When it rains, they fold so that the roots may drink. At night, they also sleep folded, to allow the heavy dew to drip from them to the roots.

The fragile, pendulous, cup-shaped flowers are each set singly on a long stalk, their five white petals decoratively veined with purple. The ovary contains a little honey, but is not very popular with insects. Moreover, since the

WOOD SORREL

flowers bloom early in the year there are but few insects about. When the flower fades, the stalk bends over and conceals the seed capsule under the leaves. When the capsule is ripe, the stalk straightens and the capsule then curls back and flings the seeds some yards distant from the parent's area. When insect pollination fails, wood sorrel has still another card to play. Hidden among the leaves are secret, inconspicuous flowers capable of self-fertilization. And as every gardener knows, wood sorrel can manage very well without seeds by means of its venturing roots. But, while it is a weed at hand, it should be enjoyed.

As the name "wood sour" implies, the leaves are pleasantly acid and they are very good in salads. In the days of King Henry VIII of England, this little herb was greatly fancied both as a salad ingredient and a potherb, and it was sold for these purposes. Gerard, the Elizabethan writer, says "and of all sauces, sorrel is the best, not only in virtue, but also in pleasantness of taste." The "Greene Sauce" was much liked with fish.

Apart from its refreshing culinary uses, this plant is rich in vitamin C and a remedy for several ailments: 1 ounce of the fresh or dried herb infused with $1\frac{1}{4}$ pints boiling water (see page 33), when cold, makes an agreeable tisane to relieve feverishness, catarrhs, hemorrhages, and urinary maladies. This may be taken freely, but excess should be avoided as the oxalic salts are not suitable to certain constitutions, especially those of a gouty or rheumatic disposition. The leaves, stems, or seeds of angelica mixed with sorrel help to mitigate the effects of the acid. (Rhubarb, too, is rendered much more acceptable to many people when stewed with some angelica, and its flavor is greatly improved.)

The familiar medieval monkish name, "hallelujah," was derived from the season of wood sorrel's blooming, the weeks between Easter and Whitsuntide when psalms of rejoicing were being sung.

The herb can be identified in many old paintings—for instance, in those by Fra Angelico. It was especially obvious as an emblem of the Trinity.

There are various opinions as to which plant is the true shamrock, the national emblem of Ireland, but wood sorrel has quite a strong claim. When St. Patrick, unable to make his savage audience comprehend the idea of the Trinity, saw at his feet the leaf of wood sorrel, he made it the symbol of the truth he was struggling to express. So, the plant became dedicated to the saint.

> O, the Shamrock, the green, immortal Shamrock!
> Chosen leaf of Baird and Chief,
> Old Erin's native Shamrock.

—Thomas Moore

Yarrow

YARROW. Yarra grass, thousand-leaf, angel flower, bunch of daisies, hemming and sewing, old man's pepper, sneezewort, woundwort, and milfoil (an obvious abbreviation of the plant's *millefolium* species label) are some of the popular names for this familiar wilding and garden weed. The most widely used of all popular names, "yarrow," is a corruption of the Anglo-Saxon *gearwe*.

We can easily see how the plant would merit the name "bunch of daisies," as it is, indeed, a member of the large daisy tribe, the *Compositae*. And yarrow has compound flowers that are borne in flat masses. Most often these are white, but occasionally the weed produces pink or rose-red blossoms.

Yarrow has the rather lilting botanical name *Achillea millefolium*. It is a venerable plant of ancient medical repute. Legend has it that Achilles was the first to take advantage of its helpful properties, when he used the weed to staunch the wounds of his soldiers who had followed him to the Trojan War. It is still used today to stop bleeding, and the plant bears its genus name, *Achillea,* in honor of the Greek chieftain.

It we were to interpret Greek legend more closely, however, it would seem that an inkling of yarrow's ability to quench hemorrhages predated the Trojan War. For it was Chiron, the gentle centaur who tutored all of

YARROW

Greece's heroes from the dawn of that culture's literature, who advised Achilles to try this remedy.

Yarrow is a lovely weed and, in fact, can compete in appearance with that other reigning beauty of the wildings, Queen Anne's Lace. The flowers are so similar that many informed people *do* mistake yarrow for its rival in beauty. Yarrow's leaves, however, are very distinct from those of Queen Anne's Lace. Dark green, and with numerous incisive divisions, they give the plant an exquisite, fernlike appearance, much like camomile. And these myriad, finely chiseled leaf segments earn for the weed its species name, *millefolium* (meaning "thousand-leaved").

Except in the poorest soils, we find yarrow everywhere —in meadows, pastures, hedgerows, and gardens, and especially along roadsides. For the plant is a perennial with a creeping rootstock that travels underground, throwing up leafy branches to produce new compact masses of foliage. Although originating in Europe, it naturalized itself to the New World soon after it was introduced here. In this it may have been helped by the American Indians who eagerly sought the little weed as a remedy for earache. In Africa and Scandinavia, too, this wilding is valued. For it is used there, instead of hops, to make a headier beer.

Yarrow has its value in the garden, where it may be encouraged so long as it is strictly desciplined. It is also a desirable constituent of mixed lawns (see page 30). In ground coverings of this type, it will contribute its rich color and velvety texture and density of growth. And these are well worth any mowing the lawn owner will have to do, to curb its exuberant growth.

Scientific observation has shown that yarrow is a genial companion plant, with root secretions that help and strengthen its more demure neighbors. At the same time, it endows these nearby plants with a more than ordinary ability to resist disease. And yarrow endears itself, also, to the discriminating cook. For it multiplies the yield of oils produced by the culinary and aromatic herbs she is growing in her kitchen garden. Just one or two yarrow plants set among these herbs will intensify their flavors and scents.

As this plant accumulates a rich store of copper plus useful amounts of nitrates, phosphates, and chlorides of potash and lime, it makes a valuable addition to the compost heap. And I hardly need mention that it makes a splendid liquid fertilizer (see page 32).

Herbalists sell dried yarrow as a medicinal aid, and it is a good one. Besides its precious mineral elements, it also contains tannin, aromatic oil, and two rare alkaloids: achillein and moschatin. (Alkaloids are a class of organic compounds valued in commercial medicines. Many of these relax the human muscles or nervous system, although the stimulants quinine, caffeine, and nicotine are also alkaloids.) Thus yarrow tea is stimulating, cleansing, and healing. It promotes perspiration when that is necessary, particularly at the onset of a feverish cold. For children it is an especially safe and effective domestic remedy, whether their ailments be the flu, measles, or other rash-causing complaints. It is also highly recommended for kidney disorders.

The tea is infused with 1 ounce of the dried herb, or a handful of fresh leaves, to $1\frac{1}{4}$ pints of boiling water (see page 33). This may be sweetened with honey and flavored with lemon. It should be taken warm in wineglassful doses every two or three hours. The same basic infusion is an old-fashioned lotion for preventing baldness, also for healing cuts and wounds. I have not yet mentioned several other of this plant's ancient names: "soldier's woundwort," "knight's milfoil," and *"herbe militaris."* These provocative labels are rooted in the herb's bygone uses when it was carried in the medical supplies for campaigners. Because I suffer many cuts and gashes from chisels, saws, and cutters, I am partial to another old name, "carpenter's grasse," and appreciate that yarrow "is good to rejoyne and soudre wounds" (from the *Grete Herball,* 1526). Enjoyable, too, is yarrow's consequence as a herb so powerful that it could cause or deflect evil according to the methods used. Witches and naughty sprites could make havoc with its help, or it could be used to make trouble for them. (It shares this ambiguity with the cinquefoil, page 120.) So, with the right and good intentions, yarrow was one of the protective herbs that were garlanded about the home, and the church, on Midsummer's Eve to thwart evil spirits at this time when they were most potent.

This kindly weed also gave solace to lovelorn maidens whose lovers were away. Ancient tradition held that if such a pining woman were to pluck a sprig of yarrow from a cemetery and repeat, while holding it, a certain mystic chant, then she would dream of her absent lover that night. The qualification was that the yarrow had to be picked from the grave of a young man. And perhaps here, too, we can see the connection with Achilles, the valiant warrior slain in the prime of his life.

Weed Control

WHEN A GARDEN is established, the best way to keep it as weedfree as possible it to use the weeds as I have suggested to enrich the compost and to benefit the gardener and his family. There is a limit to the number of times éven a weed can survive beheading and smothering. Hoeing early will kill the young weeds, and mulching the cleared ground generously with a mixture of compost, manure, leafmold, decomposing straw, rotting lawn mowings, and peat will smother their successors. Any weed defiant enough to poke through this mulch can be cut off.

Good, regular cultivation and enriching the ground with these humus-forming mulches will soon change the soil's condition and discourage the worst weeds. These will then be succeeded by annuals, which should present little difficulty to the gardener with a hoe. It is the nature of weeds to reproduce in all circumstances. On poor ground, this instinct is so urgent that, although starved, they precociously produce seed. Often the offspring of these panicked weeds are such miniatures of their kind that the gardener ignores them. Some weeds can be as small as moss and yet be prolific. But when the soil is nourishing, weeds take their time to grow to maturity, and then the gardener has a sporting chance of cutting them off before they can breed battalions of troublesome descendants.

Poisoning these unwanted plants is a bad and expensive practice except in certain circumstances. For instance, to start a new garden on a plot that is choked with the rankest weeds, such as docks, thistles, brambles, or convolvulus (a troublesome genus of twining vines) would involve years of patient labor just to get rid of these pests. In such cases a complete killer is useful to make a clean, workable beginning.

Until recently, apart from the highly dangerous arsenic mixtures, sodium chlorate was the best substance available for clearing weedy ground prior to cultivation. (And it is still useful for some purposes. For example, you can easily get rid of an isolated dock weed by slicing off its stem and putting a tablespoonful of the salty chlorate on the weed's bared roots.) But this chemical wastes months of the gardener's life. For it makes the ground acid, sterile, and infertile for six months to a year, depending on whether the soil is light or heavy. And even then, the earth has to be limed and reconditioned before you can start planting.

There is now an almost complete herbicide (weed killer) with none of those old drawbacks. This preparation is made from ammonium sulphamate, which is a crafty concoction of sulphate of ammonia (a water-soluble ammonia salt). It is effective only in spring or summer when weeds are hungrily feeding. It works through the foliage and the roots, the weeds absorbing it with relish and dying of their greed—a sort of death through over-stimulation. After about a month in the ground the ammonium sulphamate reverts to sulphate of ammonia and acts as that popular nitrogenous fertilizer. The treated area comes to life with a crop of seedlings, mostly annual weeds, which should be dug in as green manure. In only six to eight weeks the flower bed, lawnsite, or new garden plot is ready for planting or sowing. And moreover, none of the earthworms, bacteria, and other valuable soil inhabitants will have suffered. This treatment was first used by the Forestry Commission of Britain to kill such resistant things as scrub, brushwood, and the tough rhododendrons infesting plantations of their nurseling trees. It exterminates most plants, even trees, so that the instructions on the container must be meticulously obeyed.

Other complete poisons based on *simazine* were designed to clear weeds from country paths and suburban driveways. This stuff remains in the ground a few inches deep, keeping it infertile and free from any growth for about a year. These products are expensive. But when weeds are making a nuisance of themselves on paths or concrete strips rather than on arable land, then such poisons are the best answer to the problem. And the annual outlay of money is worth the saving in time (and linament) that the homeowner would otherwise spend bending over and torturously clearing his property.

Deeply rooted weeds should not be pulled out or forked up, for if plants with fine roots (such as peas and beans) happen to be growing nearby, this method of weed eradication will severely damage the delicate roots of desirable garden tenants. Roses, too, are a frequent victim of careless weeding. In his zeal to get at the offending weed, the gardener often accidentally bruises or scratches the rose roots. And this causes the rosebush to sprout new shoots from its roots or lower stems: the commonly called "suckers" that sap the bush's strength. Obviously, deeply rooted weeds should be cut out with sharp shears or a knife.

But if the gardener insists upon poisoning, there are preparations based on an ammonium compound called "paraquat" which make handweeding among roses unnecessary. These are sold under various names such as *Weedol* and *Ortho Spot Weed-and-Grass Killer*, and some come in handy aerosol-spray containers. Since paraquat works by destroying a plant's chlorophyll, these preparations act only through their green parts—leaf, stem, and shoot—and have no effect on brown bark. Thus they may be used with safety in a shrub border, under fruit bushes, and between vegetables. Paraquat is particularly useful in a rose bed for killing unwanted suckers that spring from grafted stocks. This treatment is best done in spring when both weeds and the plants desired in an herbaceous border are just beginning to grow. At this time there is enough space between them to minimize the risk of splashing the wrong target. This chemical is completely neutralized on contact with soil, so that its effect is effective but fleeting.

As soon as the ground is disturbed in any way—by birds, mice, or other animals, or by hoeing or raking after treatment—a fresh crop of weeds appears. This makes it essential that after the successful cleanup of a bed, a thick mulch be laid on as a weed smotherer. Apart from annual weeds, there are limits to the number of the chemicals victims. Some persistent types like ground elder, convolvulus, horsetail, creeping thistle, and other rogues are scarcely discouraged by one or two applications. Couch grass actually delights in it and recovers to fresh, enthusiastic growth! Perhaps when the cost and labor of repeated doses do not matter, it would eventually work on most weeds.

In a private garden the value of *selective* weed killers is exceedingly limited. They are not a substitute for good traditional cultivation and must be regarded—if at all—as emergency aids. To employ the selective, so-called hormone herbicides, you would need a large range of bottles and a great deal of expert advice on their use. They present too great a danger of corrupting distant plants because they are carried far and wide by every breeze. Moreover, some of them are made volatile in hot weather. I know, because my neighbor sprayed his field, which lies directly behind my garden hedge, with one of these hormone herbicides. A week later my shrubs and herbs were badly affected. But the effect on this farmer's weeds was negligible! There could also be the danger of build-up in the soil when these little-known concoctions are used.

Some years ago I experimented with one of these chemical "wonder-workers" on a plot full of buttercups. The plants went through such paroxysms of distortion and deformity that I was miserable with guilt. But not for long did I—or the buttercups—suffer. They revived after a few weeks. Philosophically I chopped them up and buried them deep.

I hate poisons, but I must confess that soon after I came to my present garden I did polish off a crowd of coltsfoot growing in a choice position. I painted the leaves with a brush dipped in a solution of sodium chlorate. And I cleared some nettles from the path into my little wood by putting a pinch of the same stuff, but dry, into each of their growing points. Once the land was cleared to my satisfaction, however, I went back to the tried and true method of weed control. And I have now eaten and composted so many young nettles that there are not many left. After being cut for three years they give up.

While I consider the weed killers I have mentioned to be safe when used with discretion, I know that gardeners are being constantly tempted by the unlimited choice of herbicides and pesticides offered for sale in every garden shop. We cannot assess the damage these preparations might do—until it is done. Even their makers cannot be sure until the commodities have been in use for a long time. After all, "thalidomide" began as a supposedly harmless tranquilizer. And there was the case of fluoro-acetamide, which was used in the manufacture of a systemic insecticide, "Tritox." This was sprayed on British food crops by contractors before its dangers were realized. Then, through a leak from the factory, some ground in nearby counties was so affected that the cattle grazing on it died. After Parliamentary investigation, 2,000 tons of this contaminated soil were sealed in drums and dumped like atomic waste, two and a half miles deep in the Atlantic.

As I write this I am sad and angry. My own garden, usually animated with the flickering patterns of beautiful butterflies, is bereft of all but two cabbage whites and a small tortoiseshell. I have lost one of my great pleasures. The farmers in this district hired an airplane to spray their crops with an herbicide designed specifically to kill the weed charlock. Apart from the loss of the butterflies for miles around, there are now no skylarks to sing, no lady-bugs to graze on the plant lice, and very few bees to pollinate the blossoms. What else these well-meaning farmers have destroyed cannot yet be estimated, but I am sure that in time serious damage will become obvious. When toxic sprays are used to destroy our weeds and enemy pests, they are just as surely murdering our friends, the predators of these foes—and contaminating our food, our earth, and the soil's necessary conditioners.

I say stick to the old cultural methods, hoeing and composting. And with respect and understanding, use and *enjoy* your weeds.

IDENTITY GUIDE AND INDEX

Compiled by Maryanne M. Furia

Aaron's rod, *see* Great Mullein
Abscesses, poultices for, 42, 43, 94
Achillea millefolium (bot), *see* Yarrow
Activators for composting, 15, 134; *see also* Weeds recommended in the compost heap
Adam and Eve, *see* Dead Nettle, White
Aegopodium podagraria (bot), *see* Ground Elder
African Marigold, 17: potent natural pesticide. (Bot) *Tagetes erecta. Tagetes* is a mistaken reading of the Latin word meaning "like an artemisia plant," a large genus of bitter, aromatic herbs having much-divided leaves. *Erecta* means upright.
Agropyrens repens (bot), *see* Couch Grass
Alehoof, *see* Ground Ivy
All Good, *see* Lamb's-Quarters
Allium, 22–24 (bot): a very large genus of the lily family. All grow from a bulb and hence are round and swollen in form. Other distinguishing characteristic is a pungent—and not always pleasing—odor.
Allium ascalonicum (bot): the Shallot
Allium cepa (bot): the Onion
Allium moly (bot): the Golden Garlic
Allium porrum (bot): the Leek
Allium sativum (bot): Garlic
Allium schoenoprasum sibiricum (bot): the Chive
Ammonium sulphamate, 172: an ecologically approved chemical weed killer, a compound of ammonia and sulphamic acid salt.
Anchusa, 124: name extended to 3 genera of the *Boraginaceae* family, all 3 consisting of coarse, prickly herbs. Most familiar American wilding of this group: *Echium vulgare.*

The genus name is taken from Greek *echis* meaning "viper" and indicates that the spiny foliage has made the weed uncomfortable to touch. *Vulgare* meaning "of the people" testifies to the ease with which it can be found. Producing lovely blossoms of intense blue, this weed chooses much the same habitat as Great Mullein—fallow fields, rail embankments, etc. In fact, the color of its blossoms is deepened by poor soils; *see also* Viper's Bugloss.
Angel Flower, *see* Yarrow
Anthemis nobilis (bot), *see* Camomile
Aphis, 24, 28, 134: a genus of plant lice whose special victims are fruit trees and vegetables.
Archangels, *see* Dead Nettles
Aromatic herbs, 24, 26, 75, 169: herbs having a fragrant or spicy scent and therefore often used to flavor foods or to sweeten clothing, linens, and the like.
Asthma relief, 114
Astringent properties of weeds, 88, 118, 128, 148, 158, 160, 169
Avocados, 21 (from the Spanish *bocada* meaning "tidbit" or "delicacy"): The pulpy green or purple—and strictly New World—fruit of some tropical trees of the genus *Persea*. The genus probably gets its name from the Greek hero Perseus who slew monsters. The avocado is commonly called the "alligator pear."

Bachelor's Button, *see* Tansy
Bacon Weed, *see* Lamb's-Quarters
Bacteria, soil, 28, 31, 134, 173; *see also* Activators for composting
Baldness preventative, 169

Baldur's Brow, *see* Ox-Eye Daisy
Ballota nigra (bot), *see* Black Horehound
Barbe de capucin (French for "monk's beard"), *see* Chicory
Barren Strawberry, *see Potentilla*
Batter recipes, 73
Béchamel Sauce, 138
Bee-Bread, *see* Clover, White
Bee Nettle, *see* Dead Nettle, White
Beers
  Dandelion, 65
  Stinging-Nettle, 140
Bermuda Grass, *see* Couch Grass
Birch trees, value in composting, 16
Bird's Nest, *see* Wild Carrot
Black Bindweed, 10: a troublesome twining weed of the *Convolvulus* genus; *see also* Weeds of exasperating persistence.
Black Horehound, 80: an ill-smelling, but interesting, herb of the mint family. (Bot) *Ballota nigra*. Nigra means "black."
Black Spot (on roses), 102: an extremely destructive fungus disease that causes those portions of the rose leaves not already ravaged by the black spots to yellow. Entirely ruined, the black and yellow leaves then fall prematurely from the bush.
Bladder disorders, remedies for, 57, 65, 105, 128, 150, 164; *see also* Kidney disorders and Gravel
Blue Daisy, *see* Chicory
Blue Dandelion, *see* Chicory
Blue Runner, *see* Ground Ivy
Blueweed, *see* Anchusa and Chicory
Bobby Roses, *see* Clover, White
Bonemeal, 31: important organic fertilizer consisting of crushed or ground-up bone from which all the fat and gelatin have been extracted. Also used to feed highly prized farm animals.
Borage, 26, 124: extremely common blue-flowered weed valued for its ability to soothe inflamed mucous membranes. (Bot) *Borago officinalis*. The species name means "sold in herb shops." *Borago* is Latin for "father of sprinkling" or "source of sweat" and indicates that the weed was once used to break fevers by inducing perspiration. Borage is related to the popular forget-me-not.
Bouncing Bet, *see* Soapwort
Brewing ale, history of, 93, 94
Bronchitis and bronchial complaints, remedies for, 52, 114
Bunch of Daisies, *see* Yarrow
Butter-and-Eggs, *see* Toadflax
Buttercups, 28, 29, 31: soil-robbing plants; the many-specied *Ranunculus*

genus. Buttercup plants bear bright yellow, broadly cup-shaped flowers and are totally undesirable in any garden. There are 300 different species of them; *see also* Crowfoot and *Ranunculaceae*.
Cabbage, 24, 26
Calcium deposits, dissolvement of, *see* Gravel
Calcium in weeds, 26, 31, 102, 106, 121
Camomile, 25, 26, 29, 30, 31: a valuable medicinal herb native to Western Europe. In Britain, France, and Belgium it is cultivated for its volatile oil, a prized ingredient in commercial medicines. Its healing properties extend also to plants growing nearby. (Bot) *Anthemis nobilis—Anthemis* from the Greek architectural design in which petals radiate from a perfect disc, and *nobilis* indicating what people thought of the weed: that it was noble.
Canary food, 42, 96
Cancer relief, 120
Candlewick Plant, *see* Great Mullein
Carbuncles, poultices for, 42, 43
Carpenter's Grass, *see* Yarrow
Carrots (cultivated), 22, 26, 152, 153: root vegetable, rich in vitamin A, which was carefully developed from the Wild Carrot or Queen Anne's Lace weed. Prior to 1920 its virtues were unknown in America, so it did not become a popular table vegetable here until the third decade of this century. (Bot) *Daucus carota*. The genus name is Latin for parsnips and carrots (from the Greek *daukos*). *Carota* is derived from the Greek *karoton*, also meaning "carrot."
Caryophyllaceae, 40, 127: this family contains 1,300 species including the carnation, Star Chickweed, and Soapwort. Its genera are distributed mainly in temperate, alpine, and arctic regions. All its plants are herbs. The word comes from a Latin term meaning "clovelike" or "spicily scented."
Catarrh, catarrhal inflammations, remedies for, 52, 89, 164
Cat's-Foot, *see* Ground Ivy
Cat's-Tail, *see* Horsetail
Cattle fodder, 58, 107
Chapped hands, remedy for 98; *see also* Skin lotions
Cheesecloth, 36, 43, 66, 67, 89, 130: thin, loosely woven cotton muslin that gets its name because it is used to press cheese curds
Chenopodiaceae, 108: a family of 60 species, many having cosmopolitan distribution as weeds. The word

means "little goosefoot" from the Latin *podium* and *chen*, a mistaken translation of the Greek word for hen. This family also includes cultivated spinach and beets.

Chenopodium album (bot), *see* Lamb's-Quarters

Chenopodium bonus-henricus (bot) *see* Good King Henry

Chenopodium Quinoa (bot), 106, 110: goosefoot treated as a food crop in the Andes. *Quinoa* is the Spanish version of the Quechua Indian word for this weed: *quinua*.

Chicken Pepper, *see* Buttercups

Chickenweed, *see* Chickweed

Chickenwort, *see* Chickweed

Chicknyweed, *see* Chickweed

Chickweed, 40–43: a shy, retiring member of the clovelike *Caryophyllaceae* family. (Bot) *Stellaria media* meaning "starry plant of intermediate size." Acquired its Anglo-Saxon name because of the relish birds and poultry have for it.

Chick Wittles, *see* Chickweed

Chicory, 44–47: a weed rich in inulin and sometimes grown as a commercial crop because of the richness it adds to coffee. Its leaves resemble those of the Dandelion and are also a very popular salad cress. A tasty member of the *Compositae* family. (Bot) *Cichorium intybus*. The genus name comes from Greek *kichora*. *Intybus* is the original Latin name for this weed.

Chilblain remedy, 89

Childbirth medication, 82

Chrysanthemum, 112, 115: large genus of the *Compositae* family which includes the Pyrethrums—valued for their contributions to safe commercial insecticides—as well as the Ox-Eye Daisy and the Feverfew. The name is a combination of the Greek words *chrysos* meaning "gold" and *anthemon* meaning "flower."

Chrysanthemum leucanthemum (bot), *see* Ox-Eye Daisy

Chrysanthemum parthenium (bot), *see* Feverfew

Cichorium endivia (bot): the Endive, 44, 63

Cichorium intybus (bot), *see* Chicory

Cinquefoil, 116, 118–122 (from the Italian word meaning "five" and the Latin *folium* meaning "leaf"): The weed most closely associated, in medieval minds, with witches. (Bot) *Potentilla reptans,* freely translated "creeping species of the powerful (Latin *potens*) potentilla herbs"; *see also Potentilla* and Silverweed.

Claver (from the Latin *clava* meaning "club"), *see* Clovers

Clematis, 28: a genus of vines and herbs of the soil-depleting *Ranunculaceae* family; *see also Ranunculaceae.*

Clover lawns, 30, 31, 50; *see also* Mixed lawns

Clover Rose, *see* Clover, Red

Clovers, the, 48–53 (from the Anglo-Saxon *cloeferwort* meaning "club"—specifically, Hercules' legendary three-knotted one): Weeds highly prized for their sodium content and the lushness they add to lawns. (Bot) *Trifolium repens* which describes the three-leaved, creeping White Clover and *Trifolium pratense* which describes the three-leaved Red Clover's habit of growing in meadows (up to 2 feet tall). The Clovers belong to the *Papilonaceae,* or Pea, family.

 Red Clover, 50–53

 White Clover, 30, 31, 48–50, 52

Cluckenwort, *see* Chickweed

Coffees

 Chicory, 46

 Dandelion, 64, 65

Cold remedies, 169; *see also* Catarrh remedies and Vitamin-packed weeds

Colt's-Tail, *see* Horsetail

Common Toadflax, *see* Toadflax

Complexion Aids, *see* Skin lotions and Roman cosmetics

Compositae, 20, 46, 59, 82, 98, 115, 141, 166: the largest family of flowering plants, comprising over 13,000 species. The salient characteristic of *Compositae* plants is that their flowers are crowded into heads. This family includes the marigolds, daisies, ox-eye daisies, dandelion, groundsel, yarrow, camomile, zinnia, and dahlia. *Compositae* are considered the most highly developed of the flowering plants because the arrangement of their crowded flower heads ensures the pollination of a great many blossoms by only a single visiting insect. *Compositae* comes from the Latin word *Compositus* meaning "compound." Again, this refers to the sophisticated flower head.

Compost, 13, 16; *see also* Activators for composting, Humus, and under Plant affinities—Weeds that remedy plant deficiencies

Compost heap, building of, 13–16, 57, 134

Constipation remedies, *see* Laxatives, weeds as

Consumption arrest, 62, 94, 114

Convolvulus, 17, 172, 174: a genus of twining plants commonly known as Bindweed or Wild Morning Glories.

Identity Guide and Index 🥀 179

Convolvulus (continued)
Its approximately 200 species are extremely troublesome. Because convolvulus roots sometimes penetrate 20 feet into the soil, these plants are hard to get rid of and chemical poisoning is often a necessity. The genus gets its name from the Latin verb meaning "to roll around," a description of the traveling methods of bindweed stems; *see also* Black Bindweed.

Copper in weeds, 31, 34, 42, 59, 169

Corolla, 75, 76, 85: the petals of a flower when referred to as a unit, that is, when spoken of in a collective way. The corolla may be formed of quite distinct petals or of petals that are to some degree merged together. The word is a diminutive of the Latin *corona* and therefore means "little crown" or "little garland."

Corn Spurry, 10: a small, white-flowered European weed having whorled leaves. It is a member of the *Alsinaceae* family, which contains the edible, mouse-eared chickweeds (distinct from the Star Chickweed or *Stellaria media*). (Bot) Corn Spurry: *Spergula arvensis*. The species name means "of the fields"; *see also* Chickweed.

Couch Grass, 24, 54–58, 174 (from the Anglo-Saxon *civice* meaning vivacious): Notable because it is extensive in all five continents. (Bot) *Agropyron repens*. *Repens* refers to the weed's creeping rhizome. The genus name *Agropyron* means "field and wheat," and many animals, including sheep and dogs, eat the grass blades as readily as we would eat grain.

Cowcloos, *see* Clover, Red

Cowherb, *see* Soapwort

Creamed Nettles, 137; *see also* Kitchen precautions

Creeping Charlie, *see* Ground Ivy

Creeping Jenny, *see* Ground Ivy

Cress, 42, 43, 110, 136: technically a small annual of the mustard family. Broadly used, the term refers to any herb eaten in a salad or as a sandwich garnish.

Crowfoot, 28: popular name applied to several uncultivated Buttercup species. The leaves, comprising several long, talonlike segments, reminded ancient botanists of bird's feet; *see also* Buttercups.

Crow's-Nest, *see* Wild Carrot

Culpeper, Nicholas, 48, 56, 78, 82, 93, 95, 127, 132, 133, 142, 144: dedicated seventeenth-century herbalist whose writings on plants were the medicinal

bible of his times. He is still an authority on plant descriptions and customs, and on the home remedies to be brewed from them.

Dandelion, 34, 59–68: perhaps the best-known garden weed. A powerful member of the *Compositae* family. (Bot) *Taraxacum officinale* meaning "bitter potherb sold in herb shops." Its ancient Persian name meant the same thing.

Daucus carota (bot), *see* Carrots, cultivated and Wild Carrot

Day Lily, 69–74: a splendid weed of Asiatic origins whose striking blossoms open, expand, and wilt within 24 hours. A routine food in its native continent. The almost naked stalks contrast vividly with the cluster of glorious flower heads. *Liliaceae* family. Many species. Genus name: *Hemerocallis* from Greek *hemero* meaning "day" and *kallos* (beauty). Freely translated, this means "beautiful for a day."

Dead Nettles, 75–81: bland plants of the mint family (*Labiatae*) whose leaves resemble the Stinging Nettle's leaves. (Bot) names of the four plants included in this category: *Lamium amplexicaule* for the Henbit. *Amplexicaule* refers to the fact that the Henbit's upper leaves are stalkless and appear to embrace the stem. *Lamium purpureum* (the species' name means purple) for the Red Dead Nettle whose leaves are tinged with purple. *Lamium Album* for the White Dead Nettle (*albus* being the Latin word for white). The genus tag *Lamium* means gullet in Latin and describes the tubular shape of all the dead nettles' corollas. *Galeobdolon luteum* is the botanical name of the Yellow Dead Nettle. *Luteum* means yellow, and the Greek *Galeobdolon* translated "weasel and stench" refers to the weed's unpleasant odor when crushed.

Decocting, medicinal teas that require, 46, 60, 62, 128: process of obtaining an infusion by boiling down to condense.

Dens leonis (Latin for "tooth for the lion"), *see* Dandelion

Dent de lion (French for "tooth of the lion"), *see* Dandelion

Devil-on-Both-Sides, *see* Crowfoot

Devil's-Coachwheel, *see* Crowfoot

Devil's-Flax, *see* Toadflax

Devil's-Grass, *see* Couch Grass

Devil's-Guts, *see* Black Bindweed

Devil's-Plague, *see* Wild Carrot

Diarrhea
in cattle, 101
in man, antidote for, 89, 150
Digitalis, 32: the dried leaf of the common Foxglove used to stimulate urine secretion in people suffering from dropsy and, more important, used as a valuable medicine in the treatment of certain heart conditions.
Dioscorides, 92, 114, 152: brilliant Greek physician of the first century A.D. He wrote the five-volume *De Materia Medica*, which established botany as a medical science. He also found time to serve as physician to Nero's warring legions.
Dock, 172: extremely troublesome weeds of the *Rumex* genus. Common by roadsides, but their penchant for growing in meadows accounts for the fact that they are often accidentally introduced into other types of land along with clover seed. 30 species bother North America, ¼ of them originating in the Old World. Characterized by persistent taproots, leathery seed envelopes, and brilliant flowers borne in whorls. The roots of one Dock, the *Rumex alpinus* once served as a treatment for the pains of severe influenzalike infections. Docks are related to the *true* sorrels, but not to the Wood Sorrels or *Oxalis* plants.
Dog Daisy, *see* Ox-Eye Daisy
Dog's Finger, *see* Foxglove
Dog's Grass, *see* Couch Grass
Dog's-Tooth Grass, *see* Couch Grass
Dog Tansy, *see* Silverweed
Dog Wheat, *see* Couch Grass
Drake, Sir Francis, and his famous lawn, 29; *see also* Camomile
Dried Weeds, 32, 33, 82, 83, 94, 96, 104, 134, 169; *see also* Herbalists' and health-food shops
Dropsy, remedies for, 60, 150, 152
Dry buds and flowers, how to, 73, 74
Dungweed, *see* Lamb's-Quarters

Earth-glutton, *see* Groundsel
Eczema, remedies for, 62
Eelworms, 17, 18: a microscopic variety of unsegmented roundworms. They do great damage to plant roots.
Elderberry bushes, value in composting, 16
Elizabethan Age, weed behavior and usage in, 11, 153; *see also* Gerard, John, and Tudor remedies
Embroideries, preservation of, 128, 130
Endive, 44, 63
Equisetaceae, 101; *see also* Horsetail
Equisetum arvense (bot), *see* Horsetail

Eye lotions, 43, 47, 94, 148
Ezob (Scriptural name), *see* Hyssop

Fabaceae, see Papilionaceae
Fabric cleaning, 130
False Flax, *see* Gold of Pleasure and Toadflax
False Hemp, *see* Hemp Nettle
False Horehound, *see* Black Horehound
False Mercury, *see* Good King Henry
False Motherwort, *see* Black Horehound
False Wheat, *see* Couch Grass
Fat Hen, *see* Lamb's-Quarters
Featherfew, *see* Feverfew
Fern Buttercup, *see* Silverweed
Fertilizing elements in the soil, 13
Fever, weeds that relieve, 82, 124, 164, 169; *see also* Borage
Feverfew, 82–84: weed replaced by aspirin. It has a preference for ornamenting roadsides and pining around waste areas where humans once lived. Belongs to the *Compositae* family. (Bot) *Chrysanthemum parthenium*. Genus name means "flower of gold." Species name is derived from the Greek *parthenion* meaning "maiden" and refers to both the pure white of its ray flowers and the use of this weed to cure women's problems —quite apart from its ability to tackle the complications of childbirth.
Five Fingers, *see* Cinquefoil
Five-Leaved Grass, *see* Cinquefoil
Flirtwort, *see* Feverfew
Flower conserves
Candied *rugosa* petals, 158
Conserve of roses, 159
Crystallized *rugosa* petals, 158
Flying blossoms, 132; *see also* Pesticide dangers
Folia feeds, how to make, 32; *see also* Liquid fertilizers and, under Plant affinities—Weeds that remedy plant deficiencies
Folia spray, 32, 104, 121
Formic acid, 134, 136, 137: a pungent, colorless acid found in some plants and insects, notably the secretions of ants and bees. Used in the manufacture of formaldehyde, a preservative.
Foxglove, 26, 27, 28, 146: any plant of the beneficial *Digitalis* genus. The most common is the purple Foxglove or *Digitalis purpurea* (meaning purple), whose leaves form the heart medicine digitalis. The genus name means "handlike," which fits in with its popular name (derived from the Anglo-Saxon *foxesglofa*); *see also* *Scrophulariaceae.*

Identity Guide and Index 🐝 181

French Endive, see Chicory
French Marigold, 17: potent natural
pesticide. (Bot) *Tagetes patula.*
Patula means "spreading," see African Marigold for discussion of
genus name.
Fritter recipe, 73
Fuller's Herb, see Soapwort
Fungicide, weeds as, 102, 104, 105, 134:
any substance that destroys fungi or
slows down their rate of spore
production.

Garlic, see *Allium*
Gerard, John, 42, 128, 164: English
botanist and barber-surgeon (1545–
1612). He published an herbal des-
cribing the plants important in that
era and their uses. Moreover, Gerard
had full responsibility for the
botanical gardens of the Burghley
estate, family residence of one of
Elizabeth I's most powerful ministers.
Gill, see Ground Ivy
Gill-creep-by-the-ground, see Ground
Ivy
Ginger Plant, see Tansy
Ginseng, 92: informal name for the
Araliaceae family, which contains the
Hedera or English ("true") Ivy genus.
Thus the true Ivies belong to the
same plant order as the *Umbelliferae*
family and are distantly related to
Parsley and the Wild Carrot.
Glecoma hederacea (bot), see Ground
Ivy
Gold of Pleasure, 10: a small weed of
European origin, today widely
naturalized in North America. Its
seeds yield oil and its stems are used
to make brooms. (Bot) *Camelina
sativa. Camelina* is a combination of
the Latin *linum* meaning "flax" and
the Greek *chomai* meaning "dwarf
on the ground" (a reference to the
plant's size). *Sativa* is Latin for
"cultivated."
Golden Garlic, 22, 23: a wild garlic
plant. More aesthetically pleasing
than most members of its genus, it is
often cultivated for the beauty of its
bright yellow flowers. It gives the
same nutritive properties to a humus
layer as the less attractive Alliums.
(Bot) *Allium moly.* In this case *moly*
is a Greek species name meaning
"root," see *Allium* for discussion of
genus name.
Good King Henry, 108: a weed that is
an expensive gourmet vegetable.
(Bot) *Chenopodium bonus-henricus.*
The genus name means "little

goosefoot" because it is of that
family. It earned its species label by
its popularity as a food of Tudor
England.
Goosefoot, see Lamb's-Quarters
Goosefoot plants, stinking and others,
108
Goose Grass, see Silverweed
Gout, remedies for, 46, 57, 89, 94, 120,
124, 144
Goutweed, see Ground Elder
Grafting roses, 156, 174; see *also*
Suckers
Grass, in the compost heap, 14: any
plant of the *Poaceae* family, distinguished by jointed stems, sheath-
ing leaves, and seedlike fruit. Broadly
used, grass means any green herbage,
especially herbs that provide food
for grazing animals; see *also* Mixed
lawns.
Gravel, 46, 57, 60, 150: disease causing
small masses of calcium to be formed
in the bladder or kidneys. Or the
calcium deposits themselves; see *also*
Bladder disorders, remedies for; and
Kidney disorders, remedies for.
Great Mullein, 85–89, 146 (from the
Latin *mollis* meaning "soft" and
referring to the "felty" leaves):
Illustrious member of the *Scrophulariaceae* family. Indispensable to
the functioning of medieval house-
holds and, as a medicinal herb, an
important source of cures. Great
Mullein has been identified as the
Moly of Homer and other ancient
writers. (Bot) *Verbascum thapsus.*
The species name refers to a geo-
graphic region where the weed was
plentiful in ancient times.
Ground Elder, 17, 174: extremely
common British weed that haunts the
sites of ruined castles and abbeys.
Long cultivated as a potherb and as
a cure for gout. Like the Wild Carrot,
a member of the *Umbelliferae* family.
(Bot) *Aegopodium podagraria.* The
term "foot" occurs twice in the label.
In the genus name, the Latin
podium or "foot" combines with
Greek *aigos* (goat) to say "goat and
little foot," a reference to the shape
of the leaves. The purely Greek
species name means "good for gout."
Ground Ivy, 62, 90–94: prevalent
American intruder. A member of the
large *Labiatae* family and not a
"true" ivy. (Bot) *Glecoma hederacea.*
The genus name comes from the
Greek *glechon* meaning "Pennyroyal"
(a pungent European mint) and emphasizes this weed's family affinity.
Hederacea is Latin for "ivylike," and

again emphasizes that this plant is not a true ivy.

Groundsel, 95–99: the plant that constantly "hugs the footsteps of man." (Bot) *Senecio vulgaris*. The species name *vulgaris* means "of the people." *Senecio* is derived from the Latin word for old man and refers to the white, tufted hair of the weed's fruit. *Senecio aureus* is another common American variety. Its species name indicates that the plant is golden in color.

Grundy-Swallow, *see* Groundsel

Hallelujah, *see* Wood Sorrel
Heartsease, *see* Wild Pansy and Pale Persicaria
Hedgehog Rose, *see* Wild Rose
Hedge-Maids, *see* Ground Ivy
Hedge Pink, *see* Soapwort
Hemerocallis (genus name), *see* Day Lily
Hemerocallis fulva (bot), 74: the dark-orange-flowered Day Lily
Hemming and Sewing, *see* Yarrow
Hemorrhage, staunching of, 164, 166, 170
Hemorrhoid relief, 122, 148
Hemp Nettle, 10: coarse, bristly herb whose foliage resembles that of the Nettles. Originally a European herb, it is today a common American weed. Along with the Dead Nettles, this plant belongs to the *Labiatae* family. (Bot) *Galeopsis tetrahit*. *Galeopsis* is a combination of the Greek *galee* meaning "weasel" and *opsis* meaning "appearance"; *see also* Dead Nettle, Yellow
Henbit, 75–77: a species of Dead Nettle often mistaken for the Red Dead Nettle because it so closely resembles this relative. In America, we generally call all four of the Dead Nettles "Henbit." (Bot) *Lamium amplexicaule*, *see* Dead Nettles for translation of the Latin label.
Herbalists' and health-food shops, 33, 56, 57, 58, 64, 94, 95, 116
Herb-Butter recipe, 72
Herbe de St. Fiacre, see Great Mullein
Hercules' Club, *see* Claver and Clover
Hippuridaceae 101; *see also* Mare's-Tail
Hippuris vulgaris (bot), *see* Mare's-Tail
Hoeing, 171
Hogweed, *see* Horsetail
Hollyhock rust, 104: persistent and ruinous disease attacking hollyhocks and other mallows. Characterized by spotting and discoloration of the leaves. The cause is an order of parasitic fungi.

Honey Flower, *see* Dead Nettle, White
Honeysuck and Honeysuckle, *see* Clover, Red and White
Hops, 93
Hors d'oeuvres, *see* Herb-Butter recipe
Horsetail, 100–105: a nonflowering weed, the only remnant of the once impressive *Equisetaceae* family. (Bot) *Equisetum arvense*. The genus name is Latin for "horse and bristle" and refers to the plant's uncharming appearance. *Arvense* means "of the field" and describes its habitat.
Horseweed, *see* Horsetail
Humus, 14, 133; *see also* Weeds recommended in the compost heap
Hyssop, 26: an aromatic genus belonging to the Mint (*Labiatae*) family. Its most familiar representative (bot: *Hyssopus officinalis*) is cultivated in gardens as a help to plant neighbors and a remedy for human bruises. *Hyssopus* is the Latinized form of the Hebrew *ezob*, which is mentioned often in the Scriptures. The species name means "sold in herb shops" and testifies to the herb's ancient medicinal value.
Hysteria, weeds that soothe, 144; *see also* Weeds having sedative properties

Importation of weeds to America, 88, 90, 120, 131, 145, 148
Incompatible plants and the consequences, 22, 26, 29
Indigestion relief, 43, 60, 94
Indoor flower arrangements, 28, 118, 153
Inulin, 60: a white, tasteless plant sugar contained in the roots and rhizomes of the *Compositae* family, and notably in the Dandelion.
Iron in weeds, 13, 34, 59, 94, 96, 106, 134

Jaundice remedies, 46, 94, 114, 128, 148, 150
Johnny-Jump-Up, *see* Wild Pansy
Jupiter's Rod, *see* Great Mullein

Kidney disorders, remedies for, 46, 52, 57, 65, 94, 128, 144, 150, 169
Kitchen precautions, 137
Kitchen waste, value in the compost heap, 14, 16
Knight's Milfoil, *see* Yarrow

Labiatae, 75, 93: a family of seed-bearing plants that inhabit the temperate zones mostly. The plants are usually hairy, and their hairs contain glands that secrete an odor peculiar to the family. Ground Ivy,

Labiatae (continued)
Hemp Nettle, and the Dead Nettles, as well as mint and most of our other aromatic herbs belong to this family. The name comes not from the scent, however, but from the characteristically lip-shaped blossoms of this family (from the Latin *labium* meaning "lip"). Occasionally this family is called the *Lamiaceae* from the Latin *lamium* meaning "throat" or "gullet."

Lady's-Delight, *see* Wild Pansy

Lady's-Glove, *see* Foxglove

Lady's Posies, *see* Clover, Red

Lady's-Thumb, *see* Pale Persicaria

Lamb's-Quarters, 10, 106–111: extraordinarily rich in vitamins and minerals, once the Spinach of all Europe. Member of the *Chenopodiaceae* family. (Bot) *Chenopodium album* meaning "white foot of goose." The species name describes the underside of the leaves, powdered with whitish grains. The genus name describes the leaves' shape; *see also* Chenopodiaceae and Good King Henry.

Lamium album (bot), *see* Dead Nettle, White

Lamium amplexicaule (bot), *see* Henbit

Lamium purpureum (bot), *see* Dead Nettle, Red

Lampwicks, 86

Latherwort, *see* Soapwort

Latuca sativa (bot): Lettuce, 11, 26

Lawns, *see* Clover lawns; Mixed lawns; and Drake, Sir Francis

Laxatives, weeds as, 10, 43, 46, 60, 98

Leek, *see* Allium

Liliaceae, 69: important family whose members are distributed all over the world. Most are herbs that grow from a bulb. This family includes the commercially valuable Alliums and the lovely *Hemerocallis* weeds. The family name means "lilylike," as most of them have the trumpet-shaped blooms of the *Lilium* genus, the family's best-known representative. The Greek word for "lily"—*leirion*—is the root, but its original meaning is lost in antiquity.

Lime, 13, 169: a caustic calcium substance. Probably the first agricultural material employed by prehistoric man as a soil fertilizer. Too much of it, though, makes plants unable to assimilate the other valuable elements in a soil.

Linaria vulgaris (bot), *see* Toadflax

Liquid fertilizers, 34, 57, 60, 104, 134, 169; *see also* Folia feeds, how to make

Liver disorders, remedies for, 46, 60, 148, 158

Mallow rust, *see* Hollyhock rust

Mare's-Tail, 100, 101: (Bot) *Hippuris vulgaris* meaning "horse" and "tail," refers to the plant's appearance. The *vulgaris* meaning "of the people" testifies to the weed's wide distribution; *see also Hippuridaceae* and *contrast* with Horsetail.

Marguerite, *see* Ox-Eye Daisy

Marl Grass, *see* Clover, Red

Maudlin Daisy, *see* Ox-Eye Daisy

Measles remedy, 169

Medicinal teas, formula for making, 33, 34

Medieval kitchen gardens, 63

Medieval lawns, 29, 30

Medieval vermin repellent, 84, 142

Melde (from the Old Norse), *see* Lamb's-Quarters

Mesolithic Lettuce, 11

Mexican Marigold, 17–20: the most powerful insect killer of all the Marigolds. The cornerstone of two ancient agricultures. (Bot) *Tagetes minuta*. The species name means "very small"; *see also* African Marigold.

Midden Myles, *see* Lamb's-Quarters

Midsummer Silver, *see* Silverweed

Migraine relief, 47, 89

Mildew, 104, 133: discoloration of plants by parasitic fungi. It usually takes the form of a powdery white growth.

Millepedes, 17: insect pests that feed on vegetable matter. They have cylindrical, segmented bodies with a great many tiny, almost invisible, legs. *Contrast* with Eelworms.

Mineral salts, 26, 88, 134: a white (or colorless) crystalline compound occurring as a mineral.

Mint rust, 104: a devastating fungi disease that attacks mints; *see also* Hollyhock rust.

Mixed lawns, 30, 31

Moly, 86, 88: the mythical name for Great Mullein. (The term "moly" derives from the language of the ancient Egyptians. Its Greek equivalent is mentioned in Homer's *Odyssey*.)

Moon Daisy, *see* Ox-Eye Daisy

Mouse-Ear Chickweed, 40: tiny dark green herbs of the large *Alsine* and *Cerastium* genera. Vaguely related to the cosmopolitan Star Chickweed, being of the *Alsinaceae* family. (Note, however, that some members of the *Alsinaceae* family were formerly classified in the *Caryophyllaceae*

Mouse-Ear Chickweed (continued)
group.) The Mouse-Ears have cylindrical and curved seed capsules.
Although their flowers are white like those of the Star Chickweed, the Mouse-Ear petals are cleft into 2 lobes. This accounts for the genus name *Cerastium*, from the Greek *kerastes* meaning "horned"; *see also* *Caryophyllaceae* and Corn Spurry.

Mouthwash, weeds as, 121

Muckhill Weed, *see* Lamb's-Quarters

Mulch, 22, 51, 133, 171, 174
Pine and Spruce Mulch, 26
See also Humus, and Weeds, smothering of

Mullein, *see* Great Mullein

Mullein Dock, *see* Great Mullein

Muslin, 36, 43, 66, 67, 89, 130: a soft, very thin, and finely woven cotton cloth. The name comes from Mosul, the city of ancient Mesopotamia where it was first made.

Nausea, antidote for, 144

Nematodes, *see* Eelworms

Nepeta glecoma: out-of-date (bot) for Ground Ivy

Nervous animals, 96

Nervous humans, 52, 82, 84, 114; *see also* Weeds having sedative properties

Nutrient elements, 13: mineral traces that are necessary in a soil to foster vegetative growth.

Old Man's Pepper, *see* Yarrow

Onion, 22, 24 (from Latin *unio* meaning "oneness"—in this case "a single large pearl"): Originally an Asiatic plant, today the most famous of its genus. (Bot) *Allium cepa* although there are many wild species of onion. *Allium* is the Latin name for garlic, while *cepa* is a Latin word meaning "onion," this one particular species of the garlic tribe; *see also* Allium.

Organic fertilizers, *see* Humus, Mulch, and Weeds recommended in the compost heap

Ortho Spot Weed-and-Grass Killer, 174: commercial herbicide valuable for destroying weeds that ingratiate themselves among shrubs and woody vegetables; *see* Paraquat and Weedol.

Our Lady's Candle, *see* Great Mullein

Our Lady's Flannel, *see* Great Mullein

Oxalidaceae, 162: a very small plant family of acid composition and containing the Wood-Sorrel genus, which gives the entire family its name. Most *Oxalidaceae* thrive in the tropical regions of South America and Africa. The *Oxalidaceae* are no relation to the true sorrels; *see also* Wood Sorrel.

Oxalis acetosella (bot), *see* Wood Sorrel

Ox-Eye Daisy, 112–115: ever-present weed of the *Compositae* family. Although in English-speaking lands it bears the Homeric preamble "Ox-Eye," this lovely flower was dedicated by the ancient Greeks not to Hera, but to their goddess Artemis who would have nothing to do with men. And it retained its prerogative as woman's special flower even after the Greek and Roman religions had faded. Related to the familiar, common Daisy only by being in the same plant family— for the Ox-Eye is of a totally different genus. (Bot) *Chrysanthemum leucanthemum, see* entry *Chrysanthemum* for translation of the genus name. *Leucanthemum* refers solely to the ray petals, being a combination of the Greek *leukos* (white) and *anthemon* meaning "flower." The word "Daisy" itself is a slurring of the Anglo-Saxon phrase "day's eye" and alludes to the appearance of the whole flower, golden disc fringed with white rays.

Pale Persicaria, 10: a species of the large *Persicaria* genus. Thus a member of the Buckwheat family and related to Black Bindweed. The Persicarias have hairy stems and spikelike clusters of flowers, each blossom being attached to stem by tiny stalks. The name *Persicaria* means "Persian apple" and was originally the Latin name for the peach.

Pancake recipe, 144

Papilionaceae, 50: the Pea family. Herbs, trees, and shrubs that bear fruit in the form of a pod, usually edible for either man or beast. This family is sometimes called the *Fabaceae* from the Latin *faba* meaning "bean." Formerly classified with the *Leguminosae,* but still in the *Rosales* Order. The family gets its name from the Latin word meaning "butterflylike." This adjective refers to the irregular corollas of all plants of the Pea family, which can also easily be cut into 2 symmetrical halves by a single longitudinal line; *see also* Clovers.

Paraquat, 174: a commercial ammonium compound that destroys a plant's chlorophyll, thereby making

Paraquat (continued)
it a safe herbicide to use near woody shrubs.

Parsley, 24: an herb, not a true wilding although it sometimes escapes from gardens. "Parsley" is a corruption of the genus name, *Petroselinum*, a combination of Latin *petros* meaning "rock" and Greek *selinon*, the Greeks' name for these ancient herbs. As members of the *Umbelliferae* family, the parsleys are related to many ornamental weeds; *see also* Pig's Parsley, Wild Parsley, and Wild Carrot.

Parsley Fern, *see* Tansy

Peaches, 21

Pee-a-Bed, *see* Dandelion

Persicaria, *see* Pale Persicaria

Pesticide dangers, 16
    food poisoning, 35, 176
    indiscrimate killing, 176

Peter's Rod, *see* Great Mullein

Petroselinum hortense (bot), *see* Parsley

Pig's Parsley, *see* Wild Carrot

Pigweed, *see* Lamb's-Quarters and Purslane

Pissenlit, see Dandelion

Place names derived from plants, 48, 107

Plant affinities
    aromatic herbs, their role in, 24, 25
    plant exhalations, 21, 22, 24, 26, 28
    plant root-secretions, 20, 24, 28, 29, 102
    weeds that increase storage of root vegetables, 133
    weeds that remedy plant deficiencies, 109, 133, 168, 169
    weeds that repel insect pests, 142
    weeds that stimulate growth, 21, 22, 24, 26, 27, 76, 133
    weeds that stunt growth, 22, 28, 59
    weeds that ventilate the soil, 88, 110

Plant alkaloids, 169

Plant lice, 28, 134; *see also* Aphis

Plant's Physician, *see* Camomile

Pliny, 46, 86, 98, 100, 132, 152, 153 (officially called "The Elder" to distinguish him from his also famous nephew, the historian and man-of-letters): Roman scholar and avid observer of the world about him. His *Natural History* treats all the sciences touching on man—even astronomy and primitive meteorology. Books 20 through 27 are devoted to medical botany. Pliny eventually lost his life through his dedication to the natural sciences. For he insisted upon observing, first-hand, the eruption of Mt. Vesuvius in A.D. 79 instead of fleeing to safety with the uncurious inhabitants of Pompeii and the other doomed cities.

Poison-Ivy remedy, 131

Portulacaceae, 123: small family of fleshy, succulent herbs found mainly in the tropics. Members bear seeds in capsules and often have great capability to retain moisture. The name comes from *Portulaca*, the family's most important genus; *see also* Purslane.

Portulaca oleracea (bot), *see* Purslane

Post-medieval kitchen gardens, 136

Potash, 31, 60, 162: potassium carbonate, especially that derived by filtering boiling water through plant ash. In Colonial times this was the first step in making soap. Potash and potassium are both valuable fertilizing elements in a soil and today form the constituents of many commercial nutrients.

Potassium, 13, 26, 56: a mineral element that forms 3 per cent of the earth's crust. Potassium salts are present in all fertile soils and are therefore extracted by all plants so that they form part of the plant's structure. Sugar cane, beets, and seaweed are especially rich in this element. In ancient days plants were burned so that man might extract their precious potassium compounds which were then used to make soaps, glass, and dyes.

Potatoes, 18, 21, 22, 27: the edible tubers of certain plants of the large *Solanum* genus. Of the Solanum's 1,000 species, over 100 are wild potatoes, while cultivated potatoes comprise approximately 14 species. In North America the most familiar potato is the *Solanum tuberosum*. The genus name means "Nightshade" in Latin, the name of an extremely representative plant of this genus. *Tuberosum* means "having underground swellings" and refers to the most valuable part of these plants. Potatoes have leafy foliage and both aerial and underground stems. They grow well in any soils except those with a high clay content, but prefer sandy loams rich in organic matter. Potatoes, although not necessarily the *tuberosum* species, were first found in Chile where they had replaced maize as the staple crop, being better adaptable to high altitudes. Drake (*see* Drake, Sir Francis, and his famous lawn) contends with the Spaniards for the honor of having introduced this plant to Europe. At any rate, potatoes were one of the

Potatoes (continued)
crops grown by the early colonists of Jamestown, Va. and already by 1597, Gerard had devoted much space to it in his authoritative *Herbal; see also* Plant affinities and Gerard, John.

Potentilla, 116–122: a large genus of the Rose family consisting of more than 300 species. They grow equally well in the city and the countryside, but if they had their choice, would prefer a loam soil rich in manure. The name comes from the Latin *potens* meaning "powerful" as this genus provided antiquity with invaluable medicines. The genus name has been drawn, uncorrupted from the Latin, into the English language; *see also* Cinquefoil and Silverweed.

Potentilla anserina (bot), *see* Silverweed
Potentilla reptans (bot), *see* Cinquefoil
Pregnancy inducement, 142, 144
Prince-of-Wales Feathers, *see* Tansy
Prince's Feathers, *see* Silverweed
Procelayne, *see* Purslane
Proteins, 10, 106, 134: a class of extremely complex combinations of amino acids indispensable to human life and the regeneration of tissues. Plants are an important source of protein because they can form these elements from simple substances such as the nitrates and ammonium salts in the earth. Animals cannot form them from inorganic substances, so all protein derived from animal foods was first supplied to the animal in the form of plant proteins.
Pudding recipes
Stinging-Nettle, 138, 139
Tansy, 144
Pulmonary ailments, 89, 94, 114, 150; *see also* consumption arrest
Purcelaine, *see* Purslane
Purslane, 123–126: a potherb or salad cress, originating in India and now found almost all over the world. Shows a definite preference for sandy soil and is often used as pig fodder. The name "Purslane" is probably a corruption, through Old French, of Latin *porcilaca*, a variation on the genus name. Member of the small *Portulacaceae* family. (Bot) *Portulaca oleracea*. The genus label is the original Latin name for this weed. The species name means "garden herb used in cooking." This indicates that Purslane enjoyed early use as a potherb as well as a salad green.
Pussly, *see* Purslane
Pyrethrum, 20 (from the Greek *pyr* meaning "fire" and probably referring to these plants' consuming

effects): Several showy species of the *Chrysanthemum* genus, having aromatic leaves and lilac, white, or red flowers. The African Pyrethrum, a wilding especially valued for its insect-killing secretions. This Pyrethrum is used in the manufacture of d-col, an ecologically approved commercial pesticide. As members of the *Compositae* family, this group is related to the pest-destroying plants of South America. Other Pyrethrums provide the also recommended Persian Insect Powder and Dalmatian Insect Powder. *See also* African Marigold, French Marigold, and Mexican Marigold.

Queen Anne's Lace, *see* Wild Carrot
Quick Grass, *see* Couch Grass
Quitch Grass, *see* Couch Grass

Ramanas Rose, *see* Wild Rose
Ranunculaceae, 28: a family of plants noted for the way they exhaust the soil. Most of its 700 species grow in the temperate and cold regions especially in the northern hemisphere. This family includes the Buttercups, Anemones, Clematis, Peony, and Delphinium. The term comes from the Latin word *rana* meaning "frog," because some genera of this family grow in water while other genera are land plants.
Red-Meadow Clover, *see* Clover, Red
Rheumatism, remedies for, 46, 56, 144
Rhizome, 12, 54
Roman cosmetics, 10
Rosa rugosa (bot), *see* Rugosa Rose
Rosaceae, 116: extremely cosmopolitan family of seed-bearing plants. Characterized by flowers having numerous stamens and by dry fruits. The fruits are often enclosed in pulpy receptacles. This family includes apples, plums, and strawberries as well as the Potentillas and the familiar Rose genus.
The *Rosaceae* belong to the same botanical order as the *Papilionaceae* (or Pea and Clover) family. The name is lost in antiquity, being derived from the Greek *rhodon* which was, in turn, snatched from an Oriental and Middle Eastern language.
Rose, 22, 24: plants of the erect, climbing or creeping *Rosa* genus which numbers approximately 200 species having 4,000 different varieties. These thrive in the temperate zones—especially of the northern hemisphere—but also popu-

Rose (continued)
late plateaus of the tropics and regions above the Arctic Circle. The thousands of rose varieties are explained by the ease with which they hybridize so that new roses overlap the parental species. Roses figure prominently in the songs and legends of the Age of Chivalry. They have given their name to an entire plant family; *see also Rosaceae* and Wild Roses.

Rose-Hip jam, 160, 161

Rose-Hip syrup, 160

Rugosa Rose, 155–161: wild rose of Oriental origin now at home all over America. Notable for the many hybrid rose species it has parented and for its insistence on pushing all other plants out of its way in a garden. Member of the well-known *Rosaceae* family. (Bot) *Rosa rugosa. Rugosa* means "wrinkled" and testifies that the veinlets of the leaves are sunken while the intervening spaces are elevated, *see Rosaceae* for discussion of genus (and family) name.

Rumex (genus name—the Latin word for "Sorrel"), *see* Docks

St. John's Daisy, *see* Ox-Eye Daisy

Salads
Dandelion
pissenlit au lard, 63, 64
salade de pissenlit, 63
Day-Lily, 70
Purslane, 124

Saponaria officinalis (bot), *see* Soapwort

Scandinavian beer, 168

Scandinavian fly poison, 148, 149

Scented Fern, *see* Tansy

Sciatica, relief from, 94

Scouring Rush, *see* Horsetail

Scrophulariaceae, 86, 146, 148: a cosmopolitan plant family occurring mainly in the temperate zones. Many valuable medicinal plants belong to this family, among them the Foxgloves, Great Mullein, and Toadflax. The family earned its name because years ago one of its genera was the only effective treatment for the dreaded disease scrofula: tuberculosis of the bones and lymph nodes.

Scurvy, weeds as antidote, 62, 98, 164: disease caused by lack of vitamin C in the diet. In past eras it was a real scourge among sailors long at sea, the citizens of besieged cities, and army troops on campaign.

Scutch Grass, *see* Couch Grass

Selective weed killers, 174, 175: commercial, chemical herbicides that do not kill indiscriminately but work only on certain plants. Unfortunately, one cannot control their range and they can therefore damage cultivated herbs as well as pesty plants. Sometimes called "hormone herbicides."

Senecio aureus (bot) of a particular Groundsel

Senecio vulgaris (bot), *see* Groundsel

Shallot, *see Allium* and Spring Onion

Shamrock, *see* Clover, White and Wood Sorrel

Sheepweed, *see* Soapwort

Shepherd's-Club, *see* Great Mullein

Shepherd's-Staff, *see* Great Mullein

Shepherd's Thyme, *see Thymus serpyllum*

Silver Fern, *see* Silverweed

Silverweed, 116–118, 120, 121, 122: *Potentilla anserina* (bot), a plant with extraordinarily lovely foliage. Cultivated as a root vegetable until very recently. *Potentilla,* freely translated from the Latin, means "powerful herb" and indicates that it was an essential ancient medicine. The species name comes from Latin *anser* (goose) and is either a reference to the shape of the leaves or a term of honor; *see also* Cinquefoil and *Potentilla.*

Skin lotions, 46, 98, 105, 115, 118, 121, 124, 148, 152

Skirt Buttons, *see* Chickweed

Slimming potion, 43

Snapdragon, 146: popular name for Toadflax. It is also the name used for all plants of the *Antirrhinum* genus because the blossoms when pinched in a certain way and then released make a motion like the jaws of a snapping (legendary) dragon.

Sneezewort, *see* Yarrow

Soapwort, 127–131: extremely utilitarian herb putting forth coarse pink or white flowers and closely related to the pinks (carnations) as a member of the *Caryophyllaceae* family. Soapwort leaves are still used to make a specialized detergent. (Bot) *Saponaria officinalis.* The genus name comes from the Latin word for soap. *Officinalis* indicates the weed was a stock-in-trade item of ancient herb shops; *see also* Chickweed and *Caryophyllaceae.*

Sodium, 31, 51: mineral that reduces acidity in the body and discourages constipation and gout. An important fertilizing agent in a soil, and the Clovers are an important source.

Sodium chlorate, 172: a colorless, crystalline salt of sodium. Used to clear ground of weeds prior to

Sodium chlorate (continued)
cultivation. Cannot be used once
ground is sown because it renders a
soil acid and thereby infertile.
Solanum tuberosum (bot), *see* Potatoes
Soldier's Woundwort, *see* Yarrow
Solstice flower: a plant connected with
that time of the year when the sun is
at the farthest point—either north or
south—which it ever reaches from
the earth's equator, *see* Ox-Eye
Daisy.
Sore-throat gargle, 121
Soups
Day-lily, 72
Lamb's-Quarters, 111
Purslane (English-style), 126
Purslane (French-style), 126
Stinging-Nettle, 137, 138
Sowbane, *see* Goosefoot plants, stinking
and others
Spinach, 13, 107 (corrupted through
several languages—including Arabian
—from the Persian *isfanaj*): a potherb originating in southwest Asia.
Ignored in Europe until the 16th
century, but once entrenched there it
displaced the iron-rich Lamb's-
Quarters and relegated that vegetable
to the status of a weed. As a member
of the *Chenopodiaceae* family, Spinach
is related to the Beet. (Bot) *Spinacia
oleracea*. The genus name is new
Latin for its original Asiatic name
whose meaning is lost in antiquity.
Freely translated, *oleracea* means
"edible garden herb that must be
cooked"; *see also Chenopodiaceae*
and Good King Henry.
Spinach as accompaniment to cooked
Dandelions, 64
Spring Onion, 43, 81 : early green onions
often sold under the name of
"shallots" but actually a variety of
Allium cepa.
Star Chickweed, *see* Chickweed
Stellaria media (bot), *see* Chickweed
Stew fillips, 73, 124
Stinging Nettle, 80, 132–140: member
of the very small *Urticaceae* family.
(Bot) *Urtica dioica. Urtica* is Latin
for "sting and burn" and refers to
the pain inflicted by the hairs of this
weed's stem. *Dioica* means "two
dwellings" in Latin and refers to the
fact that this weed has separate male
and female flowers that usually
occur on different plants. As a food,
extremely rich in iron, nitrogen, and
vitamin C. Valuable compost activator; *see also* Formic acid.
Stinging-Nettle porridge, 138, 139; *see
also* Puddings
Stinking Willie, *see* Tansy

Straining cloth, *see* Cheesecloth and
Muslin
Strawberry, 26, 28; *see also Rosaceae*
and *Potentilla*
Succory, *see* Chicory
Suckers, 173: accessory strength-
sapping shoots that arise, without
invitation, from the roots of a plant
or from the lower part of its stem.
Suckers must be destroyed by the
conscientious gardener in order to
preserve the health of the original
plant.
Sugar-Bosses, *see* Clover, Red
Sulphur, 13, 22, 24: a villain in the
air-pollution problem, but a good
destroyer of certain plant enemies.
Sunburn, *see* Skin lotions
Sweet Betty, *see* Soapwort
Sympathetic plants, the placing together of, 21, 22, 24, 26; *see also* Plant
affinities

Tagetes
erecta, see African Marigold
minuta, see Mexican Marigold
patula, see French Marigold
Tanacetum vulgare (bot), *see* Tansy
Tanaisie (French for Tansy)
Tannin, 88, 118, 169: strong astringent
that must be obtained from plants.
Its commercial uses include tanning
leather, constituting commercial
medicines, and serving in the
manufacture of inks and dyes.
Medically, a cure for diarrhea and
antidote to metallic and alkaloid
poisoning.
Tansy, 141–145: handsome member of
the *Compositae* family, having rich,
fernlike foliage. A common plant of
wastelands and roadsides which even
in antiquity had established for itself
a reputation for vigor. (Bot)
Tanacetum vulgare. The genus name
is a remarkably bad corruption of
the Greek term *athanasia* meaning
"immortality" and refers both to the
weed's endurance and to its use in
preserving meat and human corpses.
Vulgare is a form of "of the people"
and indicates that it was an extremely
common plant.
Taproot, 44, 62, 66, 120, 121: the main
root of a plant, usually growing
downward, which sprouts small
lateral roots.
Taraxacin, 60: a bitter, crystalline
substance extracted from the milky
juice of the Dandelion root. Used in
making commercial laxatives.
Taraxacum officinale (bot), *see*
Dandelion

Teas (medicinal)
Chickweed, 43
Chicory, 46
Cinquefoil, 122
Clover, 52
Couch-Grass, 57
Dandelion, 60, 62
Dead-Nettle, 81
Feverfew, 84
Great-Mullein, 88, 89
Ground-Ivy, 94
Groundsel, 98
Ox-Eye-Daisy, 114, 115
Purslane, 124
Silverweed, 122
Soapwort, 128
Tansy, 142, 144
Toadflax, 148
Wild-Carrot, 150
Wild-Rose, 158
Wood-Sorrel (to be drunk when cold), 164
Yarrow, 169, 170
Theophrastus, 46: philosopher who succeeded Aristotle as head of the Academy at Athens. He shared Aristotle's interest in plants and, as a naturalist, made an invaluable contribution to the botanical science of antiquity. His two immense works on plants number 16 surviving volumes in all.
Thousand-Leaf, see Yarrow
Three-Leaved Grass, see Clovers and Wood Sorrel
Thunder Daisy, see Ox-Eye Daisy
Thymus serpyllum, 30, 31: America's most familiar weed of the Thyme genus. A member of the *Labiatae* family bearing tiny, lilac, honey-rich flowers. The Thyme genus includes both cultivated plants and wildings. *Serpyllum* refers to the shape of the lancelike, ornamental leaves with their curled-back margins. *Thymus* is a combination of Greek *thyein* meaning "to sacrifice" and Latin *fumus* (smoke). It refers to ancient peoples' use of this weed to make perfumed incense; see also Weeds introduced by the Romans.
Tisanes, formula for making, 33, 34: liquid (hot or cold) having medicinal value because it has been permeated by a substance that has healing powers.
Toadflax, 146–149: yellow-blossomed weed often mistaken for the gardener's favorite, the cultivated snapdragon. Member of the *Scrophulariaceae* family. The Toadflax is distinguished from the Snapdragon genus by the long nectary it spouts at the base of the corolla. (Bot) *Linaria vulgaris.*

Linaria because its foliage resembles that of flax. Its species name, meaning "of the people," indicates the frequency with which it is found.
Tomato, 18, 21, 24, 133 (from the Nahuatl Indian word *tomatl*): Genus of fruits remarkable for their ability to control Couch Grass. Thus fall into the category of Nature's own herbicides. The genus name, *Lycopersicon,* comes from the Greek word meaning "Egyptian plant." This probably refers to its exotic appearance and the lore that surrounded it as the "Love Apple." For Tomatoes were a food of the South American Indians and were not taken outside that continent until the 16th century.
Torches, see Great Mullein
Trace elements, 13: nutrients necessary to a fertile soil although they should not be profuse.
Traveler's Ease, see Silverweed
Trèfle rampant, see Clover, White
Trefoil, *see* Wood Sorrel
Trifolium pratense (bot), *see* Clover, Red
Trifolium repens (bot), *see* Clover, White
Tuber, 70, 102: the swollen part of an underground root or stem, often used by the plant to store its food. Tubers bear tiny leaves, each having buds in their axils, so that many plants propagate themselves by means of tubers cut off from the main growth.
Tudor remedies, 60, 82
Tumors, treatment of, 74
Tunhoof, *see* Ground Ivy
Twitch Grass, *see* Couch Grass

Ulcer relief, 74, 118
Ulysses, the weed that enabled him to return home, 88
Umbelliferae, 153: plant family of 2,700 species distributed all over the world, but preferring the north temperate zone. Most of its members are herbs. The determining characteristic of this family is a flat-topped flower such as those produced by the Wild Carrot and Wild Parsnip. Ground Elder is another weed of this family. The name comes from Latin *umbella* meaning "parasol" and refers to the fact that the many ray petals spring from one point on the top of the contracted plant stem, thus giving these flower rays the look of a half-open umbrella. Sometimes this family is called the *Ammiaceae; see also* Wild Carrot and Ground Elder.
Urticaceae, 75, 140: small family of flowering plants, consisting of only

Urticaceae (continued)
41 genera. Six of these are widely distributed in North America. Most plants of the *Urticaceae* family have stems or foliage covered with hairs that sting, *see* Stinging Nettle for discussion of the family's Latin name.
Urtica dioica (bot), *see* Stinging Nettle

Velvet Dock, *see* Great Mullein
Verbascum thapsus (bot), *see* Great Mullein
Vertigo relief, 84
Viola tricolor (bot), *see* Wild Pansy
Violet fumes, 21
Violet Plates, 47; *see also* Flower conserves
Viper's Bugloss, 124: popular American name for the *Echium vulgare* weed. Deliberately introduced into Southwest grazing areas to neutralize the alkaloid content of the soil. "Bugloss" is a combination of Greek *bous* meaning "ox" and *glossa* meaning "tongue." The trumpet shape of the weed's blossoms with their prominent stamens evidently seemed, to early peoples, to be like an ox's mouth; *see also* Anchusa.
Vitamin-packed weeds
Vit. A, 62, 152
Vit. B, 106
Vit. C, 62, 136, 142, 159, 164
Vit. E, 152

Water retention, alleviation of, *see* Dropsy
Weaselsnout, *see* Dead Nettle, Yellow
Weed: any plant, edible or nonedible, beautiful or unsightly, which grows in a place where man does not want it. Weeds thus encompass herbs, shrubs, and trees. Usually characterized by exuberant growth and utter indifference to human pampering.
Weed cultivation, 50, 51, 58, 63, 88, 106, 110, 118, 123, 128, 131, 136, 141, 144, 152, 156; *see also* Medieval kitchen gardens, Medieval lawns, and Post-medieval kitchen gardens
Weed tempering, *see* Ammonium sulphamate, Hoeing, Mulch, Paraquat
Weedol, 174: commercial name of a weed killer that has as a main constituent, the chemical Paraquat; *see also* Ortho Spot Weed-and-Grass Killer and Paraquat.
Weeds as a food preservative, 142
Weeds as sweetmeats, *see* Flower conserves

Weeds as vegetables, 34, 39
Chickweed, 43
Chicory, 46
Dandelion, 64
Day Lily (tubers), 70, 72; (buds) 72, 73
Dead Nettles, 81
Good King Henry, 108
Lamb's-Quarters, 110, 111
Purslane, 124, 126
Weeds having sedative properties, 84, 89, 124
Weeds in high society, 141, 153
Weeds in magic
Circe's downfall, 88
Deterrent to evil spirits, 86, 120, 123, 170
Love charms, 95, 120, 170
Midsummer's Eve lore, 114, 170
Protection from storms, 112, 114, 123
Werewolf repellent, 120
Witches' aids and witches' banes, 86, 120
Women's problems, 112, 114
Weeds introduced by the Romans, 10, 11, 78
Weeds of exasperating persistence, 24, 172, 174
Weeds recommended in the compost heap, 26, 51, 57, 60, 80, 94, 96, 98
Weeds, smothering of, 31, 51, 57, 58, 133, 171, 174; *see also* Mulch
Werewolf repellent, *see* Weeds in magic
Wet-a-Bed, *see* Dandelion
White Goosefoot, *see* Lamb's-Quarters
White Pigweed, *see* Lamb's-Quarters
Whiteweed, *see* Ox-Eye Daisy
Whitewort, *see* Feverfew
Whooping cough remedy, 52, 114
Wild Adler, *see* Ground Elder
Wild Agrimony, *see* Silverweed
Wild Buckwheat, *see* Black Bindweed
Wild Carrot, 150–154: a weed synonymous with elegance. It springs from a fleshy, succulent root and thus gave ancient farmers the idea of further developing its most edible part. The result is today's cultivated carrot. (Bot) *Daucus carota*—because it is the same plant as, merely a different form of, the cultivated carrot. Both labels mean "carrot" in Latin, taken from the original Greek terms. Belongs to the important *Umbelliferae* family, most of which have parsleylike foliage.
Wild-Carrot Whisky, 154
Wild Pansy, 10: common intruder on European corn and wheat fields. Short-spurred flowers, usually blue or purple and mixed with white and yellow. A member of the *Violaceae* family. Our cultivated, garden

Identity Guide and Index

Wild Pansy (continued)
Pansies were developed, down through the centuries, from this persistent little weed. (Bot) *Viola tricolor*. *Viola* because it has a prominent place in the Violet genus. *Tricolor* because the blue or purple of its blossoms are always streaked with 2 other colors.
Wild Parsley, *see* Wild Carrot
Wild Quinine, *see* Feverfew
Wild Roses: rose species that need no cultivation and often get out of hand, *see* Rugosa Rose.
Wild Snakeroot, *see* Ground Ivy
Wild Spinach, *see* Good King Henry and Lamb's-Quarters
Wild Succory, *see* Chicory
Wild Sweet William, *see* Soapwort
Wines
    Clover, 52
    Dandelion (dry), 67
    Dandelion (sweet), 67
    Rose-Hip, 161
    Stinging-Nettle, 139
Wines, formula for making, 35–38
Wireworms, 17: the larvae of various species of snapping beetles; extremely destructive to plant roots.
Witch Grass, *see* Couch Grass
Witches' Ointment, *see* under Weeds in magic—Witches' aids and witches'- banes
Women's ailments, herbs for, 84
Wood ash, advantages and dangers of in the compost heap, 14
Wood Sorrel, 126, 162–165: fragile-looking plant whose trefoil leaves come directly from the rootstock while the flowers are borne singly on axillary stalks. Leaves have the property of "sleep-moving." This weed is said to have the best claim of all 3-leaved plants, to being St. Patrick's shamrock. Member of the extremely small *Oxalidaceae* family. (Bot) *Oxalis acetosella*. The genus name comes from the Greek *oxys* meaning "acid," and this tangy quality gives the weed its appeal for salads. The species name from Latin *acetum* (vinegar) confirms this description.
Wood Sour, *see* Wood Sorrel
Wormseed, *see* Goosefoot plants, stinking and other
Worms in children, 84, 98, 144
Wort, 39: a plant or herb of any kind, but especially potherbs. Derived from the Anglo-Saxon *wyrt*. Curiously, in *all* the Western Indo-European languages the words for this type of plant closely approximate our English "wort."
Woundwort, *see* Yarrow

Yarra Grass, *see* Yarrow
Yarrow, 94, 166–170 (from the Anglo-Saxon *gearwe*): an illustrious member of the *Compositae* family. (Bot) *Achillea millefolium* meaning "thousand-leaved Achilles" from the myriad divisions of its delicately segmented leaf and its connection with the Greek hero Achilles.
Yarrow lawns, 30, 31, 168
Yellow Rod, *see* Toadflax
Yellow Toadflax, *see* Toadflax